Doctors' Orders

To Margaret.
Happy Christmas,
2000!

best wishes
[signature]

DOCTORS' ORDERS

—

Dr Paul Slade
and
Christine Hall

—

BBC BOOKS

This book is dedicated to the memory of
Dr Jeremy Hallisey
1950 – 1994

This book is published to accompany the television series *Doctors' Orders*
which was first broadcast in 1998.
Executive Producer: Jeremy Mills
Series Producer: Christine Hall

Published by BBC Books, an imprint of BBC Worldwide Ltd, Woodlands,
80 Wood Lane, London W12 0TT

First published 1998
© Dr Paul Slade and Christine Hall 1998

Photographs: Craig Easton
© BBC Worldwide Ltd 1998 apart from picture on
page 176 (© Justine Dalby)
Every effort has been made to obtain permissions
for use of copyright material.

ISBN 0 563 38402 6

Designed by AB3
Text set in Berkeley and Garamond by BBC Books
Printed and bound in Great Britain by Butler & Tanner Ltd,
Frome and London
Photographs reproduced by Radstock Reproductions Ltd,
Midsomer Norton
Jacket printed by Lawrence Allen Ltd, Weston-super-Mare

Contents

Acknowledgements

I know that it is popularly believed that most people feel they have a book or a novel within them just waiting to be written, but I have to say that I never had that feeling – in fact, it would never have crossed my mind to think about writing a book before this one was suggested by BBC Books.

I must admit to having found the ominous blankness of each clean sheet of paper I've had to cover somewhat traumatic, and I must thank all those people who have eased the pain. First, our patients, because without their kind permission to include them in this book there would not have been a practice to describe. In a few cases I have changed some names in order to afford patients confidentiality.

I must also thank Andy Stewart, a fellow GP and friend from my student days, for his helpful and amusing contributions – chapters 16 and 17 are variations on his theme. My partners and all the support staff at the surgery have offered much appreciated support and encouragement and I pay particular tribute to our staff for their contributions included in chapter 5.

This preface would not be complete if I did not mention Gill, Rebecca and Justine – Daff's family – and I can do no better than refer you to chapter 18. Gill read and kindly edited the first draft of that chapter, and I thank them all for their help and hope that I have been able, in a small way, to pay tribute to an outstanding young man.

I would also like to record my appreciation for the tact and skills shown by all those involved with the making of the television documentary. What could easily have been intrusive and wearying has in fact proved to be stimulating and enjoyable, and I must particularly thank Christine Hall, the producer of the television documentary and co-writer of this book, for her intelligent and sympathetic approach.

Finally, I must thank my family for their patience and support over the last few months. This book would never have been written had my wife not continually tipped me out of my armchair and all but handcuffed me to the word processor. (The lure of the Grand Prix races, cricket and *EastEnders* would have been too much.) I thank my children for cheerfully consenting to allow me to invade the privacy of their childhood in my writings, and in my wife's case the privacy of our bedroom for filming.

At this point I feel rather like an Oscar winner at an (excruciating) award ceremony, so with a tear in my eye and a catch to my voice, I would like to thank my parents, my sister, my hairdresser, my plumber, my butcher, my baker, my…

Paul Slade

This book would not have been written if we had not been making the television series. The series would not have been made without the support and commitment of all the staff at Irnham Lodge and the people of Minehead who accepted the constant presence of our cameras. Thanks must go to the production team for their hard work: to Charlotte Desai, Lisa Silcock, Lisa Jones and Caroline Carter; to cameramen Jeremy Humphries, Jon Keeping and Clive North; sound recordists Dudley Houlden and Keith Branch; editors Alan Lygo, Ed Bazalgette and Chris Brainwood; and to Jeremy Mills, the executive producer, for his endless encouragement and advice.

Christine Hall

Introduction

Twelve o'clock New Year's Eve. I was at home with my wife, Annie, and my youngest child, Sam, at our farm in Minehead. We have four children and until this year the house had always been full of their and our friends. But this year the older children had gone their separate ways and, as we had had a big family Christmas, we decided to have a quiet New Year celebration, and anticipated a similarly quiet year. We listened to the sound of Big Ben on Radio 4 and the three of us sang 'Auld Lang Syne' and made the usual New Year wishes. Little could we know how this year was going to develop.

The first intimation was a letter we received at the surgery from the BBC telling us that they were looking at a number of general practice surgeries with a view to making a documentary series. Out of natural curiosity we agreed to a meeting and, as a result, 1997 proved to be a very interesting, challenging and unusual year. (How often do you expect to have a cameraman, sound recordist and documentary producer in your bedroom?)

Irnham Lodge is a general practice doctor's surgery and complementary health centre and is one of three practices in Minehead. There are five partners in the practice – Tim Ross, Huw Thomas, Jonathan Driscoll, Liz Thomas (Huw's wife), and myself. We cover an area of about 50 square miles from Porlock to Washford, together with some outlying patients on Exmoor. Situated on Somerset's north coast, Minehead has a resident population of about twelve thousand and a fluctuating temporary resident population during the summer that can double that figure. Our practice manages and runs the medical centre at Butlin's Somerwest World and, together with the neighbouring Harley House practice, we staff the casualty department at Minehead Hospital, where we also have in-patient beds. We are police surgeons and each of us also has a speciality, in my case ophthalmology or 'eyes'. The complementary practice, casualty, Butlin's, police work and our general practice means that the source of our labours is diverse, but the nature of the work is much the same as you will find in any surgery, whether in a city, town or village.

Our dream of developing an affiliated complementary practice had become a reality.

We moved to Irnham Lodge in April 1995 and, at the end of that year, we were able to look back on an exciting and challenging time. The move to our new premises had gone smoothly, and our dream of developing an affiliated complementary practice had become a reality. We were looking forward to consolidating those developments. Planning for the move and putting those plans into effect had been very time consuming and our first 18 months were spent establishing ourselves in a new surgery. We were all looking forward to a relaxing 1997.

Initially, we were worried that there might be a hidden agenda in the BBC's proposal – we've all read about 'the media' – but having met the producers and director we felt that their project was genuine. Next we wondered why us? Admittedly our practice may be more diverse than some, but on a day-to-day basis it is much the same as

many other small-town practices. The five partners discussed the project. We put it to the practice staff in general, spoke to some of our patients and our families and all were generally in favour. The lingering question was – why bother? It was clear that it would mean quite a lot of extra work for us all. We would not be paid for it, so was it just an ego trip? None of us harboured secret ambitions to be well known, so why agree to be filmed for nine months and appear on national television? Following further discussions with the production team we eventually decided that we really had nothing to lose. We thought that, as general practice touches almost everyone, why not open the doors and reveal all?

So we did. And while this is an introduction, it is also a time to reflect on the impact that the series has had on the practice. The most important, and I hope the most lasting, is the objectivity of the project. We have had to look at ourselves on film and in print, which is an edifying experience. As we've gone along we have had to explain to the film crew what we are about to do. To our patients we've had to explain the film crew, why they are there and what we are doing with them, and then what we are going to do for them, the patients. I hope that none of us has done anything different this year from what we would have done without the ever-present camera, but carrying out a surgery with a sound recordist and cameraman in the room keeps you on your toes. Having said that, it is surprising how quickly the presence of the film crew is forgotten. Watching fly-on-the-wall documentaries, I've always assumed that everyone has been acting, but have found that, despite the fact that a sound boom is floating above my head and a camera is circling around me, when I'm one minute into the consultation I am only aware of the patient. More surprisingly, our patients say the same thing.

I think one of the most positive things to come out of this year is the way we have all been forced to think about what we are about to do, what we are doing and what we hope to be doing. Every facet of the surgery has had to be explained. Why do we have the complementary centre? Is it just a nice idea or does it work? Do we need the extra workload of casualty and the Butlin's medical centre? It is easy to run on along the same tracks year in, year out, without questioning the wisdom of past practise. This year we have had the opportunity to look at what we do, aware that we are being observed by the very objective eye of the camera, and knowing that we will be watched and judged by a critical audience. All in all, I think I would recommend it.

My only reservation is that now we have to watch ourselves. It is a very strange thought that, having sat and watched *EastEnders*, we then sit and watch ourselves playing at being serious doctors. Of course, we take our work seriously, but we don't take ourselves very seriously and it's rather a worry. Should I ever in the future wish to appear pompous and all-knowing, my balloon may have been burst. For someone who has been in general practice for 20 years, been married for 25 and brought up and waved goodbye to three of my four children, I still don't seem to have developed the *gravitas* that I thought all adults automatically assumed at about the age of 30. My mother still has a tear in her eye when she regards the length of my hair, much as she did when I was 20. I still play in a band and – some would say sadly – think I'm still rather a hotshot on the old bass guitar. Deep down and even more sadly, I still hope that I'll be rich when I grow up. No doubt I'm in for a depressing mid-life crisis at some point – the point at which I realize that I have grown up. I think the underlying worry is that seeing myself on television may well bring that home – I'm on TV, therefore I am.

Egocentric worries aside, when I look back over the year I can see that it has been even more exciting and challenging than the previous one, and I think that in many ways we will miss the ever-present 'shadows' who have recorded the year in the surgery. It will be nice not to having to keep tidying the bedroom for 'on-call' filming and I welcome the thought of not having to talk when I stumble out of bed to make a night visit. I know I'm not alone in that – usually I fall into my car and manage to remain in a semi-comatose state until I reach the patient. This last year, we've all had to explain where we're going, why we're going and what for, and it's hard to sound vaguely intelligent in front of the cameras when it's the fourth call of the night. I sometimes wonder whether we will find ourselves talking and turning to the camera in the middle of a surgery to find that the BBC had vanished into the thin blue air months ago. I have no real doubts that we will settle back into obscurity without any problems and I can't help but think that 1998 cannot possibly offer us any increase in excitement or challenges. But next year I could always be writing, 'The first intimation of things to come was a letter from a Hollywood producer …'

1

Morning Surgery

$\mathbf{M}$y morning surgery today was pretty average, but when I look down the list of people I have seen and the problems they have presented, I am reassured that I am in the right job – I have had a thoroughly interesting time. The impression often given is that GP's surgeries are full of endless queues of people attending for coughs and colds, and wanting certificates for time off work. Of course we do sometimes see patients who have nothing more than the common cold, and over the years we have spent time, particularly with young, first-time mothers, explaining that, on the whole, modern medicine is still pretty hopeless for self-limiting viral coughs and colds and that antibiotics are not usually appropriate. We give simple advice for self treatment and five minutes spent on that pays dividends. Our patients know, firstly, how to look after themselves and, secondly, when to come and ask for help. Subsequently our surgeries are not full of patients on unnecessary visits.

For the doctors at Irnham Lodge a normal day's surgery work starts at around 8.30 a.m. We book 10-minute appointments through the morning, with a half-hour break at 10.15 a.m. The break gives us time to catch up if we have become delayed or to have a coffee while making a start on the daily paperwork. It is generally known that we may be free at around 10.30 a.m. and the common room gradually fills with the district nurses and health visitors, the practice counsellors and several other associated staff of the surgery, who often call in to chat about current problems and patients. It is a good time to keep in touch with each other. Surgery then continues on until around 12.30 p.m., when we return to the common room to sort through the daily repeat prescriptions and more paperwork, and to drink more coffee. The partners' bill for tea, coffee and biscuits is surprisingly high, although the cost is slightly reduced by our tradition of each person providing cakes and buns whenever they

The half-hour coffee break allows us to make a start on the daily paperwork and drink more coffee.

have anything to celebrate: birthdays, anniversaries and so on are all effectively announced by the appearance of a chocolate cake and cries of, 'Whose birthday is it today?' I took a supply of doughnuts in today to announce the safe arrival of a new litter of piglets born at home the previous afternoon.

This morning, after breakfast and a quick check on the new arrivals, I arrived at the surgery at 8.30 and, after looking through my messages, started surgery.

8.45 a.m. James N. James is a five-year-old boy who has been diagnosed as having attention deficit and hyperactivity syndrome. He was brought to me a few weeks ago because of his family's and his school teachers' desperation over his behaviour. From the story they gave, and from my knowledge of the family, I knew that this was more than childhood tantrums and I arranged for James to be seen by the child psychiatrist. The diagnosis was made and he was started on a very small dose of Ritalin. Ritalin is a stimulant drug that has the reverse effect on children with attention deficit and it actually calms them down. It has had a bad press in the USA, where it appears to be in much wider use, and I had some reservations about using it at first.

James's mother has brought him to see me, to let me know how he is getting on and to get a new prescription, and she is really pleased with his progress. She describes him as a different child and he is getting on really well at school, both with his teachers and with his friends. She continues, 'I've noticed that he starts getting restless towards the end of the afternoon, but he calms down by bed time and he's sleeping really well. It's a great relief because now all the family can get some proper rest.' I talk to James to make sure that he is happy with what his mother and I are discussing. At our last meeting it was impossible to get him to stay still for more than half a minute and talking with him was hopeless. He is now taking in everything that we are discussing and he tells me that school is a lot easier. He is happy to be taking his tablets, which he knows are helping him, and they do not make him feel sleepy. I give them a new prescription and I will look out for the next report from the child psychiatrist.

8.55 a.m. Eileen D. My next patient is at the opposite end of the age scale. Eileen is 80 and after a bit of a preamble about some eye irritation, she tells me what she has really come about. She plans to get married. Her 'man-friend' has been asking her to marry him for the last six months and, after a lot of thought, she has agreed. Both have been widowed for some years and they have been spending nearly all their time together. She realizes that it is a bit silly that at the end of every day they return to their separate homes. 'What we

both want,' says Eileen with a blush, 'is real companionship. We want to look after each other, and I'm hoping I might be brought a cup of tea in bed in the morning.' She is concerned about the age difference – he is in his early seventies. I am able to tell her that, despite my own tender years, I actually have some experience of the situation. Only two days beforehand I had attended the wedding of my Uncle John who, in his seventies, has tied the knot with his friend Pamela. My beloved Aunt Junie did the same thing last year, and my wife's grandfather Roy married a lifelong friend when in his seventies, to spend 10 years in happiness with her. We chatted about the situation generally and when Eileen left it was with a smile and a promise to bring me a piece of the wedding cake.

9.05 a.m. Sheila F. After two patients I am already running 20 minutes late and I am relieved when Sheila, who's 76, comes with something simple. She has dry, irritated eyes and, after a brief examination to make sure she has nothing more serious, I give her a prescription for some moisturizing eye drops and describe how she should use them.

9.15 a.m. Derrick W. Aged 56, Derrick has ischaemic heart disease. He has had angina for several years and has had two heart attacks in the past. The most recent – luckily, a small one – was a few days after a general anaesthetic for a back operation a month ago while he was still in hospital. He has made a good recovery and has come for a general check and top up of his drug supplies. He is getting some chest pain, which does not sound to be anginal to me, but he hasn't heard anything from the hospital about his next follow-up appointment and I promise to chase it up after the end of surgery. His physical examination is quite satisfactory and we go through his long list of medications.

9.25 a.m. Sharon W. Twenty-year-old Sharon has not turned up for her appointment. This is not unusual for her and I think nothing of it; in fact, I'm quite relieved because it means that I am now running on time again. She is on a regular methadone prescription and will turn up later in the surgery with an apology and an excuse. Unfortunately, at the end of surgery I find that she has a pretty solid excuse – a message in the reception book from her probation officer to tell me that she has been given a month's custody for breaking a bail condition.

9.35 a.m. Colin B. Colin is 46, and hardly ever attends the surgery – I last saw him 18 months ago with athlete's foot. However, he has been feeling very unwell for the last six days. He has a cough, a fever and a tightness in his chest. As I examine him I find that he is suffering from an attack of bronchitis but also notice that he seems extremely nervous. As he is getting dressed I tell him about his chest infection and explain how we will treat it. He is visibly relieved. 'I was sure I had lung cancer. I've been worrying about it all week. My father died of cancer some years ago and two people I know have been diagnosed within the last year.' I give him plenty of reassurance – he certainly has no other indication of it – and figuratively leave the door open for him to return if he is not entirely happy. We are generally reluctant to order X-rays unless they are really necessary, but I might get a chest film done if he returns with the same complaint.

9.45 a.m. Ken M. I usually see 73-year-old Ken with a recurring eye complaint, but he came to see me three weeks ago with a sense of constant anxiety and a feeling of physical restlessness. There was no obvious cause for it; life had been ticking along since his retirement and he had no particular worries. In fact, it was quite out of character and he was feeling that it was rather silly of him. A physical check showed that everything was normal and we had talked about family, money, daily activities, and about cabbages and kings. I had given him a small, almost homeopathic, dose of a tranquillizing antidepressant and he comes today feeling perfectly well. We arrange to reduce the tablets and stop them completely over the next two to four weeks and I'm sure he will be fine.

9.55 a.m. Kathleen J. Kathleen is 82, and within the last five years she has had both of her knee joints replaced because of severe and crippling osteoarthritis. She did extremely well after her operations and within days was back on her feet, free of pain. I saw her several months ago when she came to tell me of increasing pain in her hips, particularly on the left side. An X-ray showed that her left hip joint had almost disappeared and that the right side was also affected. It also showed that with the tilting effect of her limp she was developing some curvature of the lower spine. She has since seen her orthopaedic surgeon and has been listed for a hip-replacement operation. She lives alone and has come to discuss the arrangements for her post-operative care. With many elderly people in the area, and with many of them living alone, we are quite used to setting up a package of care in such circumstances. As soon as she is over the immediate effects of the operation we will transfer her to Minehead Hospital for convalescence. While she is there she will have regular attention from physiotherapists and occupational therapists, as well as general nursing care. Her friends will be able to call in regularly and I can see her whenever necessary. When she is fit and mobile enough to go home the district nurses and social services will turn their attention to her. Eileen leaves the surgery reassured that she will be well looked after.

10.05 a.m. Kathleen C. Kathleen is 64 years old and suffers from osteoporosis, a common condition that causes the bones to become weak and liable to fracture. Several others in her family have had similar problems and some time ago, after X-rays, blood tests and a bone density scan, she was started on a drug called Etidronate. Etidronate has been used for a long time in the treatment of a less common bone disorder known as Paget's Disease, and in the last few years it has been shown to have an arresting effect on the process of osteoporosis – it can even, in some cases, restore some of the lost bone strength. It is fairly easy to decide to whom we should prescribe the drug, but the difficulty we have is in deciding how long to keep it going. Each cycle of treatment lasts for three months and we generally plan an initial three-year course before reviewing the situation. The problem is what to do after that, as we know that if we stop the medication the osteoporosis is likely to start up again. I discuss all this with Kathleen and I arrange for some blood tests. We will probably decide to keep on with the Etidronate for now. I have a feeling that it is now accepted practice to keep patients on it for seven years, but I will talk to my colleagues and a rheumatology specialist to find out what they think.

10.30 a.m. As I'm running late again, my half-hour break has been cut down to fifteen minutes. Tim Forsey is one of our community psychiatric nurses and he comes with two of his colleagues every eight weeks to discuss any of our patients that they are currently seeing. They come at coffee-break time to catch us in the common room, and they are here today. They are just finishing with Huw, and as I put the kettle on, I scan the list of patients that I have referred for their services. Among the 12 patients there are two that I particularly want to talk about and one or two others with long-term problems who I have not seen for several months. We have a chat about them and decide who is to do what. Good communication with our fellow health workers is essential and I like the informality of Tim and his colleagues' regular visits.

10.45 a.m. John R. I am a little late starting back in surgery. The first patient is John, a short wiry man in his eighties. About five years ago, like Kathleen, he had both his knees replaced because of arthritis. He retired to this area from London and we were able to arrange his operations at St Vincent's Hospital in Pinner. I remember it well, because he went for the operations at the same time as his brother-in-law, sharing neighbouring beds, eating in the doctors' mess canteen and keeping all the hospital staff entertained by their constant chatter. I saw John a fortnight ago with pain and swelling in the right knee. He was limping quite badly and was obviously having a lot of trouble, and I had prescribed some pain killing anti-inflammatory tablets. Today, he walks briskly into the consulting room, begins waving his right leg about, and starts to dance a jig to show me that he is completely cured. I am worried that he is going to tumble and encourage him to sit down before he falls down. His knee has returned to its normal state with rest and the help of the tablets. As a token of his appreciation he tells me that he has put me on his lottery list – I look forward to his winning the jackpot!

10.55 a.m. Daisy T. Daisy is 83, and had a cataract extraction operation in her left eye six weeks ago. Her cataract lens has been replaced with a new plastic one. The eye has become sore and the lids stick together in the mornings. I sit her in front of the slit-lamp and have a look to make sure that this is no more than a conjunctivitis infection, and find that she has some signs of inflammation in the front chamber of the eye. She should have been continuing to use some eye drops after the operation, but she stopped them when the bottle ran out. I take a swab to send to the bacteriology lab and restart the drops, along with an antibiotic, and arrange to check her again in a week's time. The slit-lamp is a magnifying microscope for examining the outer and front parts of the eye. With a special lens I can use it to see the retina, and it also has a special attachment for measuring pressure within the eye. It is an expensive piece of equipment and not many GPs are fortunate enough to have one. My lamp was purchased two years ago with some of the savings money from our GP fundholding scheme, and I use it almost every day.

There are all sorts of eye conditions for which a slit-lamp examination is necessary, and by having the machine in the surgery our patients are not obliged to make the 60-mile round trip to the eye casualty department in Taunton. My partners and the other doctors in the area tend to use me to filter out cases that we can deal with ourselves, and we can avoid quite a few out-patient referrals.

11.05 a.m. Patricia T. As 39-year-old Patricia sits down she brings out a scrap of paper with a list of complaints. Patients with lists are sometimes regarded as being difficult and demanding, but I must say I rather like the idea that they have thought about the consultation beforehand and know what they want to talk about. Put in writing, things are not forgotten. It works both ways. As doctors, we often spout on at length explaining things to patients, and by the time they reach the door most of it has been mixed up in a blur of information, particularly if the subject has been complicated or distressing. My patients regularly leave the room clutching a piece of paper with my explanatory drawing on it, or a few words to remind them what to tell their family. Patricia's husband has multiple sclerosis and over the last 12 months he has had to give up work. He remains quite optimistic and puts on a brave face, but I know that Patricia is finding life very difficult, particularly with their three teenage children.

Number one on her list is a swelling in her right upper eye-lid. I examine it and find that she has a cyst in one of the grease glands in the lid, known as a chalazion. It has become quite large and irritating and if left I think she will get an abscess which will make it more difficult to deal with. I have got some ophthalmic surgery equipment, including a chalazion clamp, so I have booked her in to do the procedure in 10 days' time. Another out-patient wait saved.

We are doing a lot of minor operations in the surgery nowadays and Jonathan and I take it in turns to do a session every two weeks. Each session, which takes place in the treatment room, treats about 20 patients. Most are for the removal of minor skin lesions and we are doing an increasing number of biopsies to check for skin cancers. In the last year we have detected three cases of malignant melanoma and many less aggressive cancers.

Minor surgery in general practice used to be a sideline for the enthusiast, and I used to remove cysts and skin lesions while on duty in the casualty department. For me this was an excellent arrangement which got the job done and didn't impinge on surgery time, but in 1990 part of the new GP's contract obliged us to do minor operations on surgery premises, and the effect has been to reduce the number of normal consultations.

Number two on Patricia's list is a rash that has developed on the soles of both her feet. They are driving her mad with irritation and she can't stop rubbing them even though the relief is only temporary. On examination I see that just under the surface of the skin she has lots of tiny little blisters and in some areas they have joined together and broken down to leave cracks and bleeding. She has pompholyx eczema – pompholyx is the Greek word for blister – which sometimes affects the palms of the hands as well, though Patricia's hands are quite clear. I explain the nature of it to her and prescribe some anti-inflammatory ointment to make it calm down and clear.

Patricia then tells me that she is suffering from constant nasal obstruction with catarrh, 'And I feel so tired all the time. Do you think I've got ME?' So, we have finally got to the real reason for her coming to the surgery today. The poor thing is exhausted with all the problems that life is throwing at her and she has had enough. We talk about Roger's gradual deterioration and how it is affecting the family, their financial problems, how the children are coping with the stresses and strains that all teenagers experience, and how all this is affecting her. Amongst other things, she wants reassurance that she is physically fit enough to manage. I can do that by running a few blood checks and giving her a physical examination, but I don't have the time in a normal surgery to talk at great length. I offer to put her in touch with our practice counsellor who has both the expertise and time to help her through the current crisis and advise on how to cope in future. She is hesitant, so we agree to think about it in a couple of weeks when I will see her again to go through the results of the blood tests.

It is important for a general practitioner always to be alert to the unspoken agenda of a consultation. Patricia had very real and treatable conditions, but underlying the consultation was a real need for support through a difficult time. The time pressures on a GP, coupled with an anxiety to catch up when appointments are running late, can lead to patients leaving without having had the opportunity to get round to the underlying worry. It is remarkable how many problems are revealed when at the end of a consultation patients are asked, 'Is there anything else I can do for you?'

11.15 a.m. Jenny T. Jenny is 29, and is two-thirds of the way through her fourth pregnancy. For the second time she has opted to have her baby at home. In general our practice is fairly reluctant to encourage home births. We are 26 miles from our District General Hospital at Musgrove Park in Taunton, which means we are at least an hour

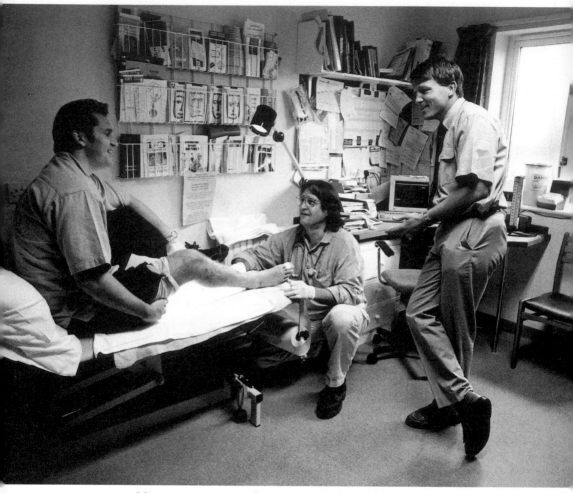

Minor surgery in general practice used to be a sideline for the enthusiast.

away from specialist help should things go unexpectedly wrong in labour or with the newborn baby. It also involves a considerable commitment on the part of the doctors and midwives to make ourselves readily available at the drop of a hat – or the breaking of the waters! We will agree however, if the circumstances are correct, to assist a mother with home birthing. It is, after all, the right of a woman to have her baby wherever she wishes, although I always encourage the prospective mother to consider the other side of that right – the duty to ensure the safety of herself and her child. I am encouraged by a recently published survey of 6000 home deliveries, which indicates that, provided the cases are well chosen and that the ante-natal care is thorough, the outcome is generally very good. The survey also indicates a high level of satisfaction among new parents – even in the event of a transfer to hospital during labour if things are not going well.

In Jenny's case there are no obstetric indications of likely problems and we have agreed to go ahead with the arrangements. We made the same plans with her last pregnancy, but with just two weeks to go she went away for the day to attend a family wedding. The best man's speech was obviously too amusing and she promptly went into labour, giving birth to a baby girl in the local hospital within four hours. She came to see me a week later with the baby, and a look of satisfaction tinged with regret that her plans for having the baby at home had not come to fruition.

Jenny has come as usual with her other three children, plus another two she is looking after during the morning for a friend who is at work. She wants her children to be fully involved with the forthcoming arrival of their brother or sister, and, after going through the routine checks on blood pressure, urine and weight, I put the sonicaid heart detector to Jenny's abdomen and the room falls silent of children's chatter while they all listen to the baby's heartbeat. I check with Jenny that she is still happy with her plans and she re-affirms her determination to have this baby at home (and confirms that she will not be going to any weddings two weeks before her due date). I am actually on holiday around the time the baby is due, but I am likely to be at home and have told Ann, our midwife, that she can call me when Jenny goes into labour. I have arranged for Huw to back me up should I be away. Ann will see Jenny in two weeks' time and I will see her again a fortnight later.

I am running 20 minutes late at this stage of the surgery which is not too bad. The next two patients are fairly brief and I am able to get back on schedule again.

11.25 a.m. Sam W. I have known 16-year-old Sam since he was a baby. His parents are good friends of the family and I am godfather to Sam's younger sister Danielle. His father suffers from asthma and Sam has inherited his allergic tendencies, also suffering from mild asthma and eczema. In general, both are under good control and, despite the asthma, Sam is an active sportsman and accomplished rugby player. He has a flare-up of his eczema and needs a repeat prescription of the emollient and anti-inflammatory creams that he uses. We have a chat about soap powders and dietary influences – ground that we have covered before – and I discover that I am seeing him later. He is coming up to the farm for dinner and to stay the night so that he and my Sam can play golf tomorrow.

11.35 a.m. Christopher D. Aged 28, Chris is a lone parent of two primary-school-aged boys. They live in an upstairs flat which is damp and is affecting the boys' asthma. We spoke three weeks ago about his council housing application, and I had phoned the housing officer to find out where they were on the list. The news is not particularly good. Because they are already in a home they keep getting by-passed by newcomers to the area who have no housing at all. The housing officer has a thankless task with ever more people on the waiting list and never enough accommodation on his books. I will write on Chris's behalf to confirm the medical situation with his boys' chest complaints and hope that it will be of help in getting them another few points on the assessment scale.

11.45 a.m. Brian G. Brian and his wife came to see me urgently four weeks ago. They had phoned as soon as the surgery opened and sounded very worried. Barbara, who was on the reception telephone, had told me about it and I had asked them to come straight up. They had recounted the events of the morning. Brian, who is 66, had woken as usual at what he thought was 7.15 a.m. and remembered making the tea.

His wife interrupted, 'No it wasn't, it was gone 8 o'clock.'

He remembered going into the bathroom. 'I wasn't quite sure why I was there, but then I realized that I had to wash, so I washed and shaved.'

Again, his wife picked up the story. 'I could hear him wandering around the house. When I got up he was standing in the lounge looking through the window. He had drawn some of the curtains back, but not others, and he had left the post by the telephone which was odd because he always brings it in first thing with the tea. He looked really strange and didn't appear to know where he was.'

'Do you remember anything of this, Brian?' I asked him. He smiled and shook his head. They went on to tell me that he had improved over the next hour or so and that he was now feeling perfectly well.

'She's more worried about it than I am,' he confided.

Brian and his wife had given a very good story of a transient ischaemic attack, or TIA. This is when a very small blood clot, or even perhaps a blood vessel spasm, temporarily obstructs the flow of blood to an area of the brain and interferes with its function. It can happen in any part of the brain and consequently can produce a wide variety of symptoms. I had examined Brian, paying particular attention to his blood pressure and the carotid arteries in his neck. Some people develop a furring-up of the lining of their arteries with a substance known as atheroma, a condition that is more prevalent in smokers and people with high-fat diets. In such cases a TIA can sometimes be caused by a small clot forming on the roughened surface of the lining of the carotid artery, and sometimes a whooshing noise can be heard with a stethoscope placed over the artery. I had found nothing wrong in Brian's case. It is an old joke that the doctor's reaction to any medical problem is 'take an aspirin, and call me in the morning'. In recent years it has been shown that aspirin, in a very small dose, has an excellent effect in reducing the stickiness of small blood-clotting cells known as platelets. By using aspirin we can reduce the likelihood of stroke and heart attack. I explained this to Brian and suggested he start taking aspirin straight away, and arranged for him to have a scan of his carotid arteries to make sure they were healthy.

He has come today for the result of the scan, and I am pleased to tell him that no atheroma disease has been found. In the meantime, he has had no further episodes of amnesia and he is feeling perfectly well. He will carry on permanently with his aspirin and I will check him again in three months' time to keep an eye on his blood pressure.

11.55 a.m. Kathleen P. I have booked the last two appointments for 80-year-old Kathleen so that I can spend some time with her without the pressure of more patients to follow. I had a letter from her solicitor last week asking for an opinion as to whether she is capable of making decisions for herself, specifically in relation to her making a will. Though I don't need to know the details, I understand that there may be some family conflict and I need to try to determine whether she has the capability of understanding the consequences of her actions. This is mainly a function of the frontal lobe of the brain.

I am extremely fortunate to have been able to call upon the services of my mother-in-law, Evelyn, who is a renowned expert in the field of mental ability in the elderly. Evelyn was a psychologist until her retirement a few years ago, and even after retirement would regularly have visits from postgraduate students from Bristol and London universities to discuss the further development of her research work. We sometimes use the 'mini-mental test'– a screening test of 20 questions – to determine the presence of a dementia type of illness, but in Kathleen's case I need more detail. Evelyn's test is known as the Middlesex Elderly Assessment of Mental State (MEAMS) and it looks at several different specific areas of brain function. I last used it a year or so ago at the request of the police and an old man's family, after they found that he had been giving away large sums of money to a 'friend'. In the knowledge that Kathleen is coming I have spoken to Evelyn so that I know what to look out for.

Kathleen knows about the test and why she is coming, and is understandably nervous. As I fetch her from the waiting room she says in her gentle Welsh accent, 'I'm petrified, doctor.' I try to put her at her ease and explain that the test is quite like a game.

First, I show her a picture. 'This woman's name is Mary Carter. Can you repeat her name so that I know you have heard me correctly?'

'Mary Carter,' she replies.

Next I show her a wristwatch, and ask her to name it and then identify some of its parts. She correctly names the buckle and the strap, and I can see that she is beginning to relax.

'I'm going to describe an object and I want you to tell me what it is. What is the name of the glass or polished surface in which you can see a reflection of yourself?'

'Mirror?' she replies, hesitantly.

'And what is the name of the hard outer case that protects animals like tortoises and snails?'

She ponders and then says, 'A cage, I should think.'

We continue on with tests of memory and perception and simple arithmetic, and then on to others, each testing different areas of brain function. The frontal lobe tests are particularly relevant.

'I'm going to give you a rule,' I said to her. 'Each time I tap once on the table I want you to tap twice, and each time I tap twice I want you to tap once. Do you understand?' She thinks for a moment and then confirms that she knows what I mean. It sounds a very simple thing to do, but in fact the thought processes involved, the ability to plan and the use of immediate memory are quite complex. We do some trial runs, which as a form of training are actually part of the test, and then I tap out a pattern of single and double taps to which she responds with no hesitation.

I continue with another frontal lobe test. 'Now, I want you to tell me the names of as many animals as you can think of, and I will tell you when to stop.'

Kathleen starts with a flourish. 'Cat, dog, rabbit, pig, horse, cow, camel ... guinea pig ...' She hesitates for a moment and then adds, 'Hedgehog. Did I say cat?' Another moment's silence. 'Did I say pig? Umm ... sheep, lambs, hedgehog ... umm ... rat ... it's an animal, isn't it? What about guinea pig? Squirrel? ... What about hedgehog?'

Her time is up. As she was speaking I was writing her answers down. The result was interesting. This is a test of the ability to hold on to a concept, in this case to stick to animal names only. It also measures something called perseveration, in other words the ability to avoid repetition, for example, 'Have I already said cat?'

I finish off the remaining tests and lastly show her the picture she had seen at the beginning of the session. 'Can you remember that person's name?'

'Mary Cart,' she answers confidently, and accurately enough to score a tick.

'The test is complete.'

She heaves a sigh. 'Thank goodness for that. I've been so worried about it I haven't been able to sleep.'

As she leaves the consulting room I hear her daughter remark, 'I noticed all the animals you chose were farm animals.'

'Well, we are farmers,' replies Kathleen.

'Yes, but we went to the Tropiquaria the other day and you never mentioned snakes ...'

'That's not an animal, that's a creepy crawly thing!'

Kathleen has generally done very well with all of the tests, but I'm not quite sure about the repetition of some of the animal names and I shall visit Evelyn this afternoon to ask about the significance of her hesitations. I will then be in a position to reply to Kathleen's solicitor with an indication of her ability to make decisions for herself.

The MEAMS test has taken almost an hour, so the surgery finally finishes at 1 o'clock. I go and see Penny in reception to check my messages and pick up my visit requests. There are some phone calls to make and a new sheaf of reports and letters has arrived in my tray. I will deal with it all this afternoon. Before that I must nip home to feed the pigs and have a quick ride around the fields on the quad bike to check the sheep and recharge my batteries. Not a bad morning's work!

2

The Other Side of the Hill

Vaccinating my four-week-old lambs the other day I took the trouble to read through the instruction sheet for the drug, checking the dosage and so on. I love the way that vets are so straightforward about naming animals' diseases. Most of these will have been inherited from the original farming names, but vets are more than happy to hang on to them. I found that, among other things, I was immunizing the lambs against black leg and pulpy kidney. Doctors would never get away with such a plain-speaking approach. It would destroy all the mystique and damage our credibility.

'Well, Mrs Smith, I've got all your test results back and they show that you have got lots-of-muscle-achey-disease.'

What I would actually say is, 'Mrs Smith, your blood tests show that you have polymyalgia rheumatica' (which literally translates as 'lots of your muscles ache in a rheumaticy sort of way').

In recent years doctors have been making attempts to demystify terms they use. Quite rightly, patients are no longer content to accept an incomprehensible diagnosis and then blindly to accept the proffered prescription. While the time taken to explain might be seen as a luxury, I have found that a clear explanation of both the complaint and the treatment is always beneficial to both doctor and patient. From my point of view I am less likely to see the patient because of minor problems that might arise in the course of their treatment. From the patient's point of view a clear picture of the complaint and the way their medication will work can prevent unnecessary anxiety when minor side-effects or the normal progress of their ailment would otherwise lead them to think things were not going according to plan. In fact, I think I would favour the veterinary style of diagnostic nomenclature being extended to our patients and may introduce some to my repertoire. A bunion on the side of a hallux valgus will be called 'hurty lump on a twisty toe'.

I'm told that as a child it was my ambition to be a vet. I spent many happy times staying on my aunt and uncle's farm in Somerset. Southtown Farm was my base in England while my parents were living abroad. I drove tractors, built hay stacks, helped with the milking and generally lived an idyllic life. I don't think there is a better way for an active child to spend his or her time than to be allowed the responsibility that a farm can afford at an early and impressionable age. Chugging round the fields on the old grey Ferguson tractor, being able to look back and see a job finished – the grass turned or the bales stacked – I learned that come rain or shine the work had to be done, and I shared in the relief when a sick animal recovered and when the hay was all safely stacked before the rain set in.

As well as the work, the farm offered the most wonderful play opportunities for me and my cousins. Death-defying bike-racing tracks all round the farm, one of which included going in through the back door, around the kitchen table, and back out again, tested Auntie Junie's patience to the limit. The finish of each race saw us flying at top speed down through the yard and up the ramp to the top of the milk stand from which the churns were loaded on to the milk lorry. The stand was, and still is, set under the kitchen window. It brought an exciting end to the timed races as it was at the top of a short stone ramp and only six feet long. We would hit it going flat out and have to stop dead or end up flying through the air and on into the rockery garden. Junie will often recall the time she looked out of the kitchen window to see me speed up the ramp to the milk stand and continue on ... and on ... By the time she got to me and my crumpled bike she had thought of and rejected many different versions of the account she was going to give to my bereaved parents. Luckily, my bike and I survived to race again.

I would sometimes meet the vet during my stays on the farm and perhaps it was watching him deal with difficult births and sort out various ailments that made me think of becoming a vet. I cannot remember when I changed my mind and settled on medicine. I suspect that it may have been when I discovered the fact that vets

Checking the sheep is a wonderful way to wind down after a busy day at the surgery.

have to get straight As in their A-levels that may have had something to do with it. (It has always struck me as strange that you have to be better qualified to train as a vet than you do as a doctor, but perhaps it is just that more people want to enter veterinary college than medical school.) In any event, I would never have gained three As or certainly would not have put myself under the pressure to gain them. I hope that at the time I had more altruistic reasons for making my choice of career, but if I did they are lost in the mists of time and I cannot really remember wanting to be anything else.

Traditionally, doctors' families seem to breed the next generation of the medical profession, but in my case I was the first. I had no real idea of what a doctor's role involved and the only contact I had had with the medical services was when I had my eyebrow and nose sewn back together after a close encounter with a barbed wire fence. (I had screamed blue murder throughout the whole procedure and to this day have a particular sympathy when suturing a child in casualty.) An inclination towards the sciences rather than the arts at school, a liking of people and a preference for doing, rather than being done to, resulted in me following my ambitions and going on to train at Charing Cross Hospital Medical School.

Happily, after 20 years in practice I can say that it has proved to be not such a bad choice. A GP will never be rich, but will always be comfortable. Hours can be long and night calls get harder as I get older but there is never a dull day. I never know what I am going to do or who I'm going to meet during a surgery and, as I hope this book will show, each 'routine' surgery will usually throw up something or someone interesting. As our practice has expanded we have all found our interest has been renewed as each development has come along. Our complementary centre has certainly opened my eyes to the value and efficacy of alternative treatments and the time we spent considering and developing the new premises introduced me to many committed and skilled complementary practitioners. I know that I am lucky to be able to say that I have never been bored by my work; I may have been exhausted both physically and mentally, but never bored.

I am also lucky that I have been able to set up a mini Southtown Farm of my own, and so stress is never really a problem as far as I am concerned. If I have a difficult day I can come home and race the quad bike around the fields, although we don't have a milk stand to complete the fun. Feeding the pigs and checking the sheep is a wonderful way to wind down, and even the mundane chores of fence mending and muck clearing have a therapeutic effect. I can even play vet at times, and while I admit to talking to my lambs I do not go as far as to explain the meaning of pulpy kidney or black leg to them. I just get on and vaccinate them – a bit like the baby clinic on Friday afternoons. Just as the lambs stand quietly with their mothers, the babies lie sleeping and then I walk in and stick a needle in them. At least the lambs seem to forget as soon as I've finished, while the poor babies have quivering bottom lips for quite a while and nothing I do or say can win a smile. When I leave an immunization clinic to a chorus of crying babies the idea of being a vet is rather appealing, at least it is until I'm up in the small hours lambing in a cold and often wet shed. The grass is always greener on the other side of the hill ... although I have to admit that on reflection mine is probably sufficiently verdant.

3

Live Stock – Dead Stock

The gestation of a pig is exactly three months, three weeks and three days – exact enough that you don't need to worry about the number of days in the month or take leap years into account. Consequently, it was no surprise that my son Sam phoned me in surgery this afternoon to announce that I had become the 'father' of 15 squealing piglets.

My friend and farming mentor Roger Webber lives nearby at Hindon Farm. Roger is a proper farmer with a big tractor and a huge flock of sheep. He and his wife Penny run a mixed arable and stock farm on the opposite side of North Hill. They also have a thriving country holiday business on the farm. As well as the sheep they keep a herd of pigs – a mixture of Gloucester Old Spots – like my four-year-old sow – and Saddlebacks, and a Welsh boar with the appropriate name of John Thomas.

Just four months ago I took the Land Rover and horsebox over to Hindon to collect John Thomas and bring him home to service my sow Patience. This has become an annual event and a joke between Roger and me that John Thomas takes his holiday of sun, sea and sex at Greenaleigh each year. When I arrived, Roger announced that JT had his suitcase packed and ready and that he was looking forward to his vacation with eager anticipation.

Enticing a fully grown boar away from his harem and into a strange horsebox is not particularly easy. It's rather like trying to eat spaghetti with a knife when you have been on a diet for a week. You chase it frenetically around the plate and just when you think you have landed a mouthful, it slithers off to join the rest at the bottom of the dish. It looks up at you smugly as if to say, 'Ha, think you're in control, eh?' After we had chased the stubborn beast for a good 20 minutes, slopping through the boot-high slimy mud, JT's memories of the previous year suddenly came flooding back. He stopped

I am lucky that I've been able to set up a Southtown Farm of my own.

running around, sniffed the air and twitched his tail, and ambled slowly up the ramp into the trailer. Having completed the Ministry of Agriculture paperwork in the farmhouse kitchen over a cup of coffee, I bade farewell to Roger and Penny and drove John Thomas home.

With the temptation of a bucket of pig-nuts I led him with no difficulty towards the sty and introduced him to his consort.

'Patience, this is John Thomas – John Thomas, this is Patience. I do believe you have met before.' Patience greeted JT with a grunt and a shove with her nose and walked off in the opposite direction. John Thomas started slathering. I had no wish to intrude so I left them to it. The results of John Thomas's holiday are 15 healthy piglets, and no runt. Patience will do her best to lie on and suffocate some of them, but I am well pleased.

Before we moved to the farm we had a house on the outskirts of the town. Set in an acre of land, it enabled us to play at farming on a small scale and we set about creating a practical interpretation of the story-book version of life on the farm.

First came the chickens. They had been sold off by a factory farm, having been judged to have passed their commercial lay-by date. Having spent all of their short lives inside, with movement severely restricted, we rather anticipated that they would do the chicken equivalent of a whoop, run gleefully around the small paddock and excitedly investigate their pristine hencoop. In fact, the change was clearly too much to handle, and for two days they huddled together in a corner of the coop and nothing would tempt them to come outside. On the second day the huddle had edged towards the coop door and we managed to entice them out with a pile of choice pickings. They did eventually rediscover their instincts and happily roamed around pecking and clucking. Their eggs were plentiful, a lovely flavoursome deep yellow and, being pre-salmonella days, we were able to provide a local campsite with free-range eggs.

No one had any problem eating the eggs. Eating the chicken was another matter. It was not the principle of eating meat that was the problem. We had resolved that issue by having an experimental vegetarian week. Instead of relying on meat and two veg some thought had to go into the meals and very creative vegetarian alternatives were served up. However, by day three the first rumblings of revolt were being voiced by the children. Our three-year-old, having carefully dissected his vegetable stew, set down his knife and fork with a question that has now gone into family folklore: 'Where's my meat?'

He hit the nail on the head as far as I was concerned. The meals were very nice but something (meat) was missing. We completed the seven days but it only served to strengthen our carnivorous instincts.

But when it came to eating our own chickens, the children were adamant and no amount of explaining that all the chicken they ate was *someone's* chicken could change their minds. I was determined to be less sentimental, but there was one little hurdle I just could not get over. Once it was dead I would have no problem with plucking, gutting, cooking and eating the chicken, but it was that 'once dead' that proved the sticking point. Two attempts to approach the coop with a manly 'hunter/gatherer' stride to my step had left me relieved that I was in an age that allowed me to stroll out to the supermarket to hunt only for bargains. So there was no free-range chicken stew. Those that the fox allowed to survive eventually died of old age. In fact over the 15 years we have been playing at farming, only one goose out of the large number of chickens, ducks and geese that we have kept has reached the kitchen table. Goosey Loosey secreted himself behind my car as I was reversing one morning. The poor old bird showed no external sign of injury but was clearly dead. I realized that on this occasion I had got over the 'once dead' problem and that weekend we sat down to a very tasty, if a little bruised, roast goose.

Next came the lambs. We acquired a couple of orphaned lambs that required bottle-feeding and, being our first lambs, the whole family lost their hearts to them. They were named and loved. It was clear that these lambs would definitely not end up in the freezer – or, at least, not in our freezer. Rearing Hengis and Horsa proved to be fairly trouble free and so we decided to increase our flock to three. The next poor little thing was in a sorry state and had to be brought into the house in an attempt to keep him warm. He was made a nest by the side of the kitchen boiler where he lay shivering and plaintively bleating. At first it was difficult to persuade him to take his bottle, but eventually he did start to pick up and as he gained strength wobbled around the kitchen, his skinny little legs not looking strong enough to support him. He was still too small and weak to go outside, and the practical problems of turning the kitchen into a lamb pen revealed themselves in all his vivid yellow droppings and smearings. He was quickly restricted to one area of the room in a pen made by cobbling together a fireguard and a stair-gate. (Far better the children run the risk of being burned or falling down the stairs than the lamb spread his sweet-smelling droppings all over the kitchen floor.) One evening just before he was fit enough to move outside, he had been particularly messy, having managed to break out of his pen and wander freely around the kitchen. We sat watching television and an advertisement came on which exhorted us to buy a particular brand of kitchen cleaner because 'it cleaned the

The results of John Thomas's holiday are 15 healthy piglets.

germs you can see and the germs you can't see'. I pictured our kitchen at that moment and couldn't imagine being in a position where I would be worrying about the germs I couldn't see when I needed a high-power hose and a yard brush to begin to clean the kitchen floor.

However much you enjoy your job it's always a great relief on a Bank Holiday weekend when you wake up on the Monday morning and realize that you can actually have a lie-in. Nevertheless, when I turn over to try and resume sleep my mind runs through all the jobs I have to do around the farm and I find it impossible to lie still for a moment longer. I have a strong urge to leap out of bed in order to make the most of the day. I know that my teenaged boys don't have this trouble, so it must be due to my age.

My first job today is to attend to one of my young lambs. She was born three weeks ago with twisted hind legs. Unable to stand, she was incapable of feeding from her mother and things were not looking good for her. There were two options – I could either knock her on the head and end her misery, or I could commit myself to a lot of work and attempt to mend the twisted legs. Being squeamish and a bit of a sentimental old fool I chose the latter option. I milked some colostrum from the mother and fed it to the lamb. You know at the beginning whether you are likely to succeed with a project like this. Some lambs make no effort and are bound to die; others, like this one, are fighters. She eagerly drank the milk from a baby's bottle and searched for more. After advice from the vet, I made up some splints for her back legs and strapped them on. After a while she got used to them and was able to move around, but though she was penned with her mother she could not keep standing long enough to suckle. For the next 10 days I milked the mother and bottle-fed the lamb, and as she gained in size and strength I thought I was winning. Then her front legs gave out and I had to move the splints from the back legs to the front.

For the last week she has been feeding herself and trying to keep up with the others and it is time to remove the splints. As I walked out into the barn I caught sight of her strutting around in a goose-step type of walk, trying to keep up with the other lambs that frolicked around her. I sat down with her on the side of a trailer and anxiously removed the bandages. The knee joints still felt weak and I seriously doubted the value of the efforts of the last three weeks. I tentatively placed her on the ground expecting her to fall in a crumpled heap on the floor. For a few seconds she stood and wobbled to gain her balance and then walked off slowly to find her mother. She will be fine and I am chuffed.

My experiences of part-time farming have not always been so successful. When we moved to Greenaleigh, a 30-acre smallholding on the coastal side of North Hill, we were able to expand our livestock, and my birthday present that year was a Gloucester Old Spot piglet. Anyone looking at a young piglet must find it hard to relate the appealing little creatures with their delicate, even elegant legs, to the huge and ungainly beasts they will become. Patience, as she was to be named, was presented to me with a birthday bow wrapped round her middle. She had the run of the house for the afternoon of my birthday and it was perhaps this indulgence that led her to always believe she had a right to come into the house whenever she managed to escape her sty.

Usually we would be warned by her grunting and snuffling and could persuade her to come away from the house by shaking a bucket of pignuts and a giving her a hefty push in the right direction. As Patience grew, pushing became useless. A full-grown Old Spot sow weighs two-and-a half hundredweight and has a very distinct mind of her own. Although she had a perfectly good sty she was always on the lookout for ways to escape. Once out she would amble around the farm causing great consternation to walkers following the footpath through the yard. She had no sense of fear and would happily lumber up to nuzzle a leg and hope for a back scratch. Toggles on shoes were viewed as a particular delicacy and were snuffled up and swallowed in a flash. We didn't need a guard dog; we had a guard pig.

Our guard pig seemed to have let us down one weekend. The family had been out for a picnic and on returning home we found the front door open and inside were faced with a scene of devastation. Tables and chairs were overturned, books were all over the floor where the bookcase had been emptied, and in the kitchen there was smashed china by the upturned table and the contents of the laundry basket were scattered all around the room. We had had burglars.

We were just composing ourselves to set about finding what was missing when a familiar grunting and snuffling was heard coming from the direction of the dining room. Pushing open the dining-room door we saw Patience, wastepaper basket wedged on her head, blindly stumbling around the room. By following her trail from the front door we reconstructed her destructive progress. As greed was always her guiding light, we assumed that the wastepaper basket had held an apple core. The basket had become firmly wedged on her head and poor old Patience was effectively blindfolded and, no doubt, frightened. That, together with her bulk, meant we really had

Even on my day off I have a strong urge to leap out of bed and get started on the jobs around the farm

escaped lightly. Apart from the china, nothing had been broken. Patience was remarkably keen to get back to her sty that evening and, while she has made the odd attempt on the house since then, it never seems to be with quite the same enthusiasm.

Twelve years later, the spirit of Patience still lives on in her offspring. We are still playing at farming but playing a little more seriously. We have one or two litters of piglets each year and although they are no longer named or allowed access to the house the appeal of a litter of young piglets never diminishes. Our flock of sheep now numbers 30, and while weak lambs still have to be taken inside to keep warm, they most certainly do not have the run of the kitchen.

As with everything, you learn by your mistakes and one of the first things I learnt was that there was a lot to be said for my father's often-repeated statement:

'Where there's livestock, there's dead stock.'

I began to suspect my father might be wiser than I had given him credit for when, under pressure from the children, we embarked on a record-breaking collection of pets. I have no problem with the dogs – faithful, housetrained, an encouragement to go for a good long walk, they live out their natural life spans. I definitely have a problem with cats, which seem to live forever, but would take a cat any time in preference to guinea pigs (eight), rabbits (four), mice (10), rat (one), stick insects (four), budgies (five), tortoises (two), goldfish (seven). Of those 41 beloved pets only the tortoises, two of the guinea pigs and a rabbit are not buried under twig crosses, tied together by one grieving child or another. The tortoises had the good sense to make a run for it and were never seen again. The Jack Russell ate two of the guinea pigs. The rabbit was purely and simply a miracle. Safely tucked up in his hutch one night, the next morning he had metamorphosed into a rather fine ferret. Whether the ferret feasted on Bright Eyes the rabbit before moving into the hutch, I have no idea, but there he was and there he decided to stay for a few weeks. Then, just as he had appeared overnight, one morning he had gone. The rabbit's grieving owner was rather miffed that the rabbit didn't come back in his place.

Along with our late pets, the poultry seemed to have a very fragile hold on life. I have decided that golden pheasant drop dead just for the hell of it – too cold, too hot, too quiet, too noisy, any excuse! The chicken, ducks and geese could not really be blamed for their own demise – blame lies fairly and squarely with the foxes. Despite the fact that we have had to give up keeping poultry because of the foxes, my family resolutely refused to allow me to shoot them. Consequently, one particular fox would casually wander up to the yard and stare me out while he considered which choice bird to consume. The family would be alerted to my intentions by my rushing into the house and scrambling to load my gun, all the while issuing forth foul curses on our bushy-tailed friend. Before I could get back outside, my supportive family would be there clapping, screaming and generally setting about scaring off the fox. In the event, what usually happened as a result of their noise was that a golden pheasant would drop dead with fright, the chickens would get their feathers thoroughly ruffled and not lay for days and the fox would casually stroll down the field, to return for his supper as soon as our backs were turned.

The geese faired no better as far as the foxes were concerned. Our first gander was the most terrifying creature one could hope to meet, and if any goose were going to defeat a fox it would be him. His normal state was one of violent dislike of everything and everyone, but at springtime, when his geese were sitting on their eggs, he became a Homicidal Maniac. The geese always made their nests in a barn that opened out on to the farmyard, through which runs a public footpath. Ninety-nine per cent of the people who walk through are very pleasant and we have no problem with the footpaths that cut through the farm – it is the other one per cent that gives walkers and ramblers a bad name. For some reason some walkers seem to think that because a farm has a public footpath running through it, the public has a right to poke about the barns. However, as annoying as this may be, it was these 'one-percenters' who unknowingly provided us with an unusual and extremely enjoyable spectator sport. On fine spring afternoons the family would seat itself in the garden and wait for a 'one-percenter' to walk through the farm. If we were nice people we would have warned them not to poke about the Homicidal Maniac's barn, but we are not nice people. The laughs we've had when a 'one-percenter' has wandered into the barn to reappear a short time later with the HM in hot pursuit are too numerous to recall. He never caused any physical damage, but I rather hope he made his victims reconsider the wisdom of trespassing on private property.

Poor old HM. He reigned supreme when the opposition was walkers (as above), my wife and daughter (trapped in the car by him for an hour before being rescued), or my mother (attacked while defenceless, carrying in the washing). These victories must have led him to believe he was invincible, so when Foxy Loxy turned up he was somewhat unprepared. As I've explained, one of our foxes had a relaxed attitude towards man. As far as he was concerned, if he was spotted, I would rush into the house, the family would run out making a lot of noise and then, when I reappeared with my metal stick, we would all go back into the house arguing. On the evening of HM's finest hour the fox appeared and for once HM was not with his geese. The usual regime was that each evening he would escort his harem one by one to the stream, where they would have a long drink before returning to their eggs. This evening he was caught settling one concubine back onto her nest, leaving concubine number two unprotected. The fox took his opportunity, and with one leap fox and goose tumbled down the field.

HM could not have moved faster, and before we could do anything he was off down the field to protect his mate. The family's shouting and clapping had no effect. My shooting into the air had a similar lack of effect: fox and gander would not have noticed if we had set off a cannon. Eventually, I separated them by charging down the field, yelling at the top of my voice and waving my arms, a sight that would terrify anybody. HM lay winded and bleeding. The fox ran out of reach but, defiantly, only just out of reach. We carried our gallant gander up to the house and placed him in a box by the Rayburn. He died within the hour. Another little twig cross was placed on the hill.

Left to their own devices the remaining geese were picked off by the fox one by one and our best endeavours were to no avail. The last goose went to meet her maker one summer afternoon. I returned home from afternoon surgery to find her half-eaten carcass lying in the farmyard. As I entered the house I could hear Delphine, our French au pair, in floods of tears.

'It's all my fault. I'm so sorry. It's all my fault.'

'No, no. There was nothing you could have done. You are not to blame.'

'It's all my fault.'

Delphine was, and is, a saint. For the last four months she had put up with our four children, withstood life without mains electricity, survived the cat regularly messing in her room (not to mention on top of her chocolate cake) and, despite homesickness, had maintained a Gallic stiff upper lip. The death of the last goose had apparently been the breaking point.

I set about reassuring her. It was not her fault. I made her a cup of tea and kept reaffirming that there was nothing she could have done. It was just one of those things. She was not to blame herself. Cup of tea drunk and tears wiped away, an apparently restored Delphine went off to collect the children from school.

Half an hour later the children arrived home with a smiling Delphine in tow.

'Feeling better?' I enquired.

'Oh, yes. You were so nice. If I had crashed *my* father's car he would have gone mad.'

I looked out of the window and the battered car confirmed there had been a slight misunderstanding! As I had kept repeating, Delphine was completely blameless with regard to the demise of the goose (she hadn't even known it was dead), but was indeed solely to blame for the car accident in town that morning.

I have been a mite unfair to the foxes, as they are not the only reason for our decision to give up poultry keeping. A few years ago we had a healthy flock of laying hens and a broody hen happily sitting on a clutch of peacock eggs. The eggs were due to hatch at any time and it was with great anticipation that the hen box was checked each morning. One morning as I approached the box I could see that the lid was not secure and wondered whether the chicks had hatched and the activity caused the lid to slip sideways. Lifting the lid I came eyeball to eyeball with a satiated badger and I'm not sure which of us was more surprised to see the other. The broody hen was dead and the eggs crushed and licked clean. I tipped the box on its side and watched as the badger waddled off through the yard, disappearing through a hole in the hedge and on up into the woods. He would be back!

Every evening I would go down to the chicken run to collect the eggs and lock the hens away for the night. This particular evening I was forewarned of the disaster by there being no background clucking as I approached the run. As I got closer I saw that the ground was littered with dead hens. The corpses showed no sign of having been eaten – just killed. At first I assumed that the fox had got into the run, but a movement in the top corner caught my eye and there was the badger, chicken at his feet, feathers in his mouth. I stared at him and he stared at me. I told him that if he were still there in five minutes I would be going to fetch my gun. Returning in five minutes he *was* still there and I told him in no uncertain terms that he had been warned and when I came back with my gun he would be shot – protected animal or not. When I came back with my gun he showed no signs of having taken my warnings to heart and of course I couldn't shoot him. (I was brought up on *The Wind in the Willows* and Badger was a good old chap.) Again, I watched him as he waddled off.

We didn't replace the poultry – foxes, badgers and Edwina Curry made them more trouble than they were worth – but I do miss seeing the hens wandering around the farmyard and there is nothing quite like a home-reared free-range egg.

4

Time and Motion

One of the advantages of living and working in a small town like Minehead is that I don't have the commuting problems suffered by so many people getting to work. While we may have to travel considerable distances to visit our outlying patients when on call, day to day everywhere we need to go is within a three-mile radius. Consequently, I can snooze in bed, confident that I can get to the surgery within 20 minutes without fears of traffic hold-ups. The usual routine is to doze to the strains of John Humphrys and Sue MacGregor and when 'Thought for the Day' starts I know that I must leap from my bed, shower, dress and make for my car. The trouble is, I never take into account what I might meet on my way to the car. If I'm lucky it's just a rat on the front-door mat (a gift from one of the cats) and I can delicately pick it up by its tail and chuck it into the garden. More seriously, it can be the sight of a litter of piglets running amuck in the garden. I know if I leave them, marital harmony will be a thing of the past. As far as the garden is concerned I'm the brawn, my wife is the brain and the sight of her borders and lawns after 13 piglets have snuffled and nuzzled for any length of time has to be seen to be believed. With warning cries of 'sausages', 'chops' and 'parsley-and-thyme stuffing' they have to be rounded up and put back with their mother. More seriously still, sometimes the car decides not to go or one of the children has left it in town where they took it last night. All these events seem to occur on almost a regular basis, and, on reflection, I'm not sure why I don't take them into account when setting my morning timetable, but I suppose my natural optimism leads me to hope for the best.

My wife (and I suspect the surgery receptionists might agree) claims that I have a pathological inability to get anywhere on time. I don't agree that I'm always late, but I do wonder if I had some time-related trauma in my early years, as time-keeping is sometimes a problem. I don't wear a watch, priding myself on my skills in time estimation. A glance at the sky and I'm usually right to within 10 to 15 minutes. As I leave everything to the last minute, being 10 to 15 minutes out in my estimations means I'm often running late. The result is that, having found suitable transport – in this grave emergency my trusty, rusty bicycle – I turn up at the surgery somewhat harassed and hot and running 15 minutes late. As I stride in, I try to have a busy, concerned expression on my face in the hope that I might fool everyone that I've been dealing with some emergency. No one is fooled and, grabbing a coffee, I collect the first patient (in every sense of the word).

My first patient, 49-year-old Brenda, has been a patient for over 10 years. Five years ago she came to me with mood swings, flushes and night sweats, which were becoming increasingly troublesome. The symptoms were consistent with her going through her menopause and a blood test to measure her hormone levels confirmed the diagnosis. We discussed the ins and outs of hormone replacement therapy and, after checking that there were no reasons for her not to take it, I started her on a low dose of a mixture of oestrogen and progestogen hormones. After a few weeks and some adjustment of the preparation, she was much better and she has been very happy taking it ever since. Like all our patients who are taking HRT she comes for a routine check of her blood pressure and weight every six months and at her last check with me two months ago everything was fine and I gave her a repeat prescription. I was therefore a little surprised to learn three weeks ago that she had suffered a thrombosis in her right arm and had been admitted to hospital. She made a full recovery and has been started on an anticoagulant treatment called Warfarin. Warfarin therapy has to be frequently monitored by blood testing and Brenda is having one or two tests a week to keep the dosage levels correct. She has come for another test today and I want to use the opportunity to review whether she should still be taking the HRT. I saw from the hospital discharge report that she had not been advised to stop it.

A history of thrombosis can be a reason not to take HRT and I discuss this with Brenda, pointing out the increased risk associated with smoking, an unfortunate habit of hers. She was horrified at the thought of not taking the HRT. On a couple of occasions in the past she has stopped or missed it for a while and her symptoms, particularly of depression and mood swings, have returned with a vengeance and made life quite intolerable. At the moment, while she

When I look down the list of patients today, I am reassured that I am in the right job.

is taking Warfarin, she is perfectly safe and we have decided to continue the HRT. After a one-off episode of thrombosis we would normally stop the anticoagulant treatment after six months so we have time to decide what to do later in the year. It is a difficult decision, so I will definitely take advice from my consultant colleagues on this nearer the time.

My next patient, Vernon, who is 79 years old, is also taking Warfarin and has done so for over ten years. His blood clotting is now very stable and we check his level every two months. Vernon is an ex-RAF and civil aviator and has come today for a routine review of his blood pressure, for which he is taking some fairly mild treatment.

'How are you today, Vernon?' I politely ask.

'Farting with confidence, thank you,' he replies, and in response to my quizzically raised right eyebrow he goes on to explain.

'It's a phrase we used to use to the medical officer in India. When there was a lot of Delhi belly about you could only fart with confidence if you felt perfectly fit.'

Reassured by the self-assessment of his overall condition, I measure his blood pressure and issue a repeat prescription.

I have never met the next patient before. In fact, no doctor has ever met Harold before in a professional capacity. He is 72 and this is the first time he has ever passed through the portals of a doctor's surgery. Harold retired some years ago as a council workman for one of the London boroughs and moved to Minehead two weeks ago to live near his son and family. He is accompanied by his daughter-in-law, or, I should say, has been coerced by his daughter-in-law into coming. She has threatened dire consequences should he refuse. She and her husband have noticed that Harold becomes breathless very easily and is suffering from headaches. He, of course, denies it but when I enquire about his exercise tolerance it becomes clear that he is quite limited in his activity.

'How far can you walk, Harold?' I ask, and in response to his non-committal answer: 'Can you manage the hill from the High Street up to your house without stopping?'

He agrees that he has to take a rest every hundred yards or so.

'What about getting upstairs?'

'I haven't got any stairs,' he replies, still managing, defensively, to ignore his symptoms.

I know that I will have to be very unthreatening to encourage his re-attendance and, after a gentle examination, I chat to him about how he is settling into his new home. Harold's blood pressure measurement is rather high and he is showing some early signs of heart failure. I arrange to get some blood tests with Jenny, our practice nurse. At the same time she will run an ECG test. I also give him a request form for a chest X-ray and get an agreement with him that he will return to see me in a week's time to go through the results so that we can decide if he needs any treatment. I have a strong suspicion that he will not come back of his own accord, but I am confident that we will eventually build up a worthwhile support.

Barbara is my next patient and she is lying on the couch in Jenny's treatment room. Barbara comes in every six months for a hormone implant, which I insert under the skin of her lower abdomen. She has been having them for several years and Nina, our ex-partner who left the practice two years ago, had always performed the procedure. Although I was always competent in the general principle of subcutaneous implants, I had never done a hormone implant before meeting Barbara. Barbara needs to have one-and-a-half pellets inserted and, as I am preparing the equipment today, she reminds Jenny and me of my first attempt. The pellets are very small and have a waxy appearance. I assumed that they were soft but as I went to cut the little pellet with a scalpel blade I found it to be very hard and brittle and difficult to cut in two. As I applied more pressure on the pellet it suddenly snapped, pinged against the side of the metallic kidney dish and shot across the room, disappearing under the desk. Breaking the pellet in half is rather an imprecise measurement of dose. Barbara finds that the effect of the implant starts running out after a little over five months so she now always gets the larger of the two pieces (which I cut under a gauze swab to prevent embarrassing egress of the medication) and an appointment for 24 weeks instead of 26.

Mary has come for a check of her blood pressure. A few weeks ago she came with a general feeling of tiredness and headache and it transpired that she had ceased her treatment for mildly raised blood pressure. I encouraged her to get back on to her treatment and she is now well again. I got to know her well some years ago in difficult circumstances when her husband was terminally ill with pancreatic cancer. He was a retired GP from Scotland and a truly gentle man who bore his illness with great fortitude. His spirit was a great lesson to all of us who cared for him and somehow he managed to make us feel privileged to have done so. Mary is an active member of one of the local women's groups and was very helpful when my daughter Nicola was raising money to go abroad after her A-levels. Nicola went to Brazil to teach English with an organization called Project Trust and Mary's group gave some sponsorship on the understanding that she would give a talk to them on her return. Mary and I always catch up on the latest family news and she tells me that her daughter has recently been to Holland on a cycling holiday. We are thinking of doing the same thing this year and she is going to ring me with the address of the travel agency.

I have to bring the pleasantly domestic chat to an end and move to collect the next patient from the waiting room. Nathalie came to Minehead two years ago at the age of 18 to escape a childhood of physical and sexual abuse. She was already on large doses of prescribed tranquillizers and was constantly drinking too much. When drunk she would become very violent. She was capable of inflicting considerable damage on her friends and her surroundings and she was in regular contact with the law. She had a big scare six months ago when she almost ended up with a custodial sentence and that was when I first met her. She came to an emergency surgery in an attempt to get more Valium to see her through the crisis. I wasn't feeling particularly sympathetic at the time – she was at the end of a surgery that had been especially full and I had had a long day. I find the best way to deal with the sense of frustration in such circumstances is to lean back in my tilting office chair and give in to the knowledge that this may take some time. It was time well spent. After several long follow-up sessions Nathalie is making a huge effort to improve herself and her lot. She has taken herself off the Valium and has had no drinking binges for the last six weeks. She is going to the gymnasium and is losing weight and feels quite proud of herself. Best of all, she is making plans for the future. She has thoughts of going to college to get qualifications for nursing and is also thinking of applying to join the army. I have really done little more than to give her my time and show some respect and understanding, but she tells me that it has made all the difference. When I reflect on the stable, happy home that I was fortunate enough to be brought up in, one can have a great respect for someone who has had to take a hold of their chaotic life and has found the strength of character to build a future for themselves.

John has spent a lifetime of sociability around the whisky bottle and the beer pump and it is all catching up with him. He suffers from ischaemic heart disease, which causes him anginal pain and breathlessness with exertion and he has had to retire early because of his worsening health. He has never regarded himself as an alcoholic because he knows that he can go without drink if he wants to. The only trouble is that until now, despite my encouragement, he hasn't wanted to. His weekly alcohol unit intake certainly exceeds the World Health Organization's definition of alcoholism.

I have been keeping an eye on the state of his liver over the last couple of years with occasional blood testing and, until recently, he has shown no significant abnormality. Therein lies the problem. If you keep getting normal test results the doctor's obviously a fool and doesn't know that you can cope with it. It almost gives tacit approval to continue with the bad habits. John began getting symptoms of liver failure three months ago, with a slight yellowing tinge to the whites of his eyes and increased ankle swelling. The blood tests confirmed the situation and I was really quite hard on him. Complete abstinence was required – no 'occasional odd one'. He has taken to his new lifestyle like a duck to water and actually enjoys the sense of achievement that his self-denial brings. His liver tests are improving and I am confident that they will return to normal within six months. He is already feeling much fitter and this will stand him in good stead should he come to require surgery for his heart disease. I will continue to monitor him even after his liver has recovered. He knows that we have a sneaky test that shows whether you are drinking or not!

Ian is an old friend from the rugby club. He was a leading light in the setting up of the mini-rugby for the Minehead Barbarians 15 or more years ago and I have had many hilarious nights in his company. He is barely more than five feet tall, and him looking over the top of his squeeze-box accordion with his beaming smile is an unforgettable memory for us and our French rugby friends from Brittany.

Ian started to experience a hand tremor five years ago and went on to develop Parkinson's Disease. The drug therapy for Parkinson's takes several forms and can be quite complex – getting a patient on to an even balance of medication can be difficult. Too little medication and the tremor and freezing of movement make life intolerable – too much, and the side-effect of excessive uncontrollable movements of the limbs is equally difficult. On different days the same dosage of medication will seem to have varying effectiveness. Most of the medications have a fairly short time of action, so patients often have to take their pills many times a day, and to get a close control of their symptoms it is essential that they have a full understanding of their disease.

Ian is well informed. He gets regular information from the

Parkinson's Disease Society and he has a very good working knowledge of the pharmacology of his therapy. He knows the purpose of each of his tablets, so that he is able to tailor his treatment effectively, and his use of the terminology would not be out of place at a pharmaceutical convention. I found this to be a little disconcerting at first – after all, we doctors are the ones who are meant to be telling him what to do. Even his neurologist now acknowledges that Ian knows best and we largely let him get on with it.

A fairly crude but useful measure of the state of a patient's Parkinson's is to see his or her handwriting. Ian has come today with a neatly written list and flow-chart of his current medications and their timings and, although I offer some advice, he is already well ahead of me!

The consulting room was full for my next and last appointment. Anna and Phillip are both profoundly deaf and have brought their five-year-old son Jason with them as well as Jackie, the RNID interpreter. I sometimes see Anna on her own and we manage to understand each other quite well with a combination of lip-reading and hand gestures, occasionally resorting to a note-pad and pen. But for important medical consultations social services provide an interpreter, and today Anna and Phillip do not want to risk misunderstanding anything I say as they have come to see me about Jason.

Jason has recently developed a lump on the side of his head and a few weeks ago Anna and Phillip took him to see the consultant in Bristol. I last saw Jason just before he went for the scan and they have come to see me today to discuss the next stage. I know they are all worried about Jason's condition and Anna's anxiety clearly shows on her face. I explain to them that the scan showed a cyst underneath the surface of Jason's skull about an inch across.

Anna asked what that meant. 'Is there going to be pressure on his brain?'

I tried to reassure her. 'It is not a brain tumour, but there is a possibility there might be pressure on the brain. It's important for you to see the neurosurgeon who can talk to you about it in detail. If it does need to be treated there may be some sort of operation to drain or remove the cyst. As far as I'm concerned, it's a very rare condition and I've never seen a patient with it before. But I can tell you that Jason doesn't have a life-threatening condition.'

As well as making sure that the worried parents have all the information they need, I am only too aware that we have a little five-year-old sitting listening and watching us the whole time. It is very easy to talk over the top of a child's head, forgetting how much he or she can understand, and to underestimate the worries they have, particularly when they are the subject of the conversation. I make a point of including Jason and try to explain things in a way that he will understand. It can be a difficult balance. Children are not stupid – they know if the wool is being pulled over their eyes – but they also need a degree of protection. Jason knows that he has a lump on his head and that we need to find out why. He understands what a scan is and that he will need further treatment. Happily, I am able to reassure him as well as his parents. They have an appointment with the neurosurgeon in a few weeks and I will keep in touch with Jason's progress. Anna is also 16 weeks into her fourth pregnancy and so I will be seeing her regularly for ante-natal check-ups.!

The last time I saw Anna and Phillip, it was not in the surgery but in one of our local pubs where I was strutting my stuff with our rock and blues band Breech of the Piece. They are the most perfect audience and if I had a modicum of modesty where the band is concerned, their enthusiasm would bring a blush to my cheek. Popular opinion (confirmed regularly by my nearest and dearest) is that we are a mite loud. For Anna and Phillip, the feel of the thudding vibration of my bass guitar is perfect, and while the volume prevents normal conversation, for once, with their sign language and lip-reading abilities, they have the advantage over the rest of the audience.

As an impecunious medical student, the forced sale of my bass guitar to pay for bread and a month's rent on a garret room, had put paid to my ambitions for stardom. I had not played any rock music for some 20 years, but when my sons started twanging, I bought a cheap bass guitar to accompany them. Dave, our lead guitarist, runs a music shop in town and one day while I was in buying some acoustic guitar strings, he told me he was putting a new band together and that they were in need of a bass. Following a rehearsal in which the rest of the band – Tim on vocals and guitar and Roger on drums – failed to detect my complete lack of talent (or were too desperate and polite), I was asked to join and Breech of the Piece was formed.

We play two or three times a month in local pubs and clubs and at private functions and have a great time. A recent booking was for a fund-raiser at the Wembley Arena of West Somerset (otherwise known as the Winsford Village Hall) and after the show one of the organizers, a local farmer, came on stage as we were clearing our equipment. As he pumped our hands he thanked us in his broad Somerset accent.

'Great show, boys. Marvellous, marvellous. You were fantastic!'

'I'm glad you liked it,' I said when it came to my turn.

'Oh no, I di'n like it!' he said, 'but the rest of 'em did.' And he booked us for next year.

Music therapy has a lot to recommend it

Music therapy, in the form of mellow blues or the thrashing of a Thin Lizzy track depending on the mood, has a lot to recommend it and I always look forward to a gig or the weekly rehearsal in Roger's studio.

At the end of surgery, I call into the office to pick up my messages, phone calls and home visit requests. Penny and I go through them and I make a list of the return calls I have to make. One of the messages is from Annie to see if I am coming home at lunch-time as the piglets and their mother are out in the garden and cannot be persuaded back into the barn – also, the garage has phoned to say that my car will not be ready until tomorrow. That's a bit of a pooper! I was relying on getting the car back to speed my progress around town. As I walk out to my trusty rusticle, I calculate that it is about one o'clock, so I can get home to sort out the pigs, pick up Annie's car (if she's not working this afternoon) and be back for the afternoon vaccination clinic by 2.15.

Penny sticks her head round the back door: 'Paul, I've just had to book you an extra emergency appointment. I've put it in at 1.45. Hope that's OK.'

'Fine.'

Cycling off, I recalculate that I can get back home by 1.15, and if the pigs are not too stubborn I can still be back in time. As I pass the old town hall clock I see that it's 1.15 already! I go up a gear and pedal faster.

5

Dragons at the Door

No record of a doctor's practice would be complete without due consideration being given to the important role of the receptionist and the support staff in general. The proverbial doctor's receptionist is a domineering, dragon-like woman, intent on denying the patients access to their doctor. In fact, it is a very difficult role, which requires tact, endless patience, absolute discretion and the ability to do many things at any one time. The receptionists have to balance the needs and demands of the patients with the needs and demands of the doctors – often not an easy thing to do.

Rather than write only from the doctor's perspective I asked our support staff to consider their role and to offer some insights into their working lives. Within the week I found a large envelope on my desk and as usual, my load was lightened by the helpful, thoughtful and efficient responses. Just as when we moved practice premises, I was overwhelmed by the personal commitment and involvement shown. During the move every member of staff gave up their weekend to help – it was far more than any employer could expect and highlighted just how lucky we are to be living and working in this community. The success of the new surgery had become everyone's project and everyone rolled up their sleeves and got on with what needed to be done so we could have the doors open on Monday morning without any hitches being obvious to the patients. So when I asked for comments for this book, a night out was organized and an enlightening insight to life behind the receptionist's

counter was produced. I think that I can do no better than to offer
Barbara Dyer's thoughts on life at the surgery, the result of that night
out with the receptionists, secretaries and two practice nurses.

'We calculated that between the 12 of us we had spent a total
of 119 years working at the surgery. In light of the fact that
doctors' receptionists have such a poor reputation, we all
cheerfully agreed that the job couldn't be all that bad for us to
have withstood it so long – an average of 10 years apiece!
There is no doubt, however, that this is no job for the faint-
hearted. In fact the following qualities should be looked for
when viewing a prospective employee:

1. Nerves of steel.

2. An ability to be prepared for any medical eventuality in the
waiting room – from listening to Mrs Smith who is worried
that she may catch something while sitting there, to dealing
with a cardiac collapse on a Saturday morning when the doctor
is in casualty or on home visits and you are working alone.

3. Three pairs of hands, and two pairs of ears for simultaneously
dealing with a phone call from a patient and verbal instructions
from a doctor on an entirely different subject.

4. Hawk-sharp eyesight to spot doctors trying to sneak out of
the building without picking up their messages.

5. A fast pair of legs should the above happen when you are on
the telephone and you need to jump in front of their car before
they truly escape.

6. Strong willpower to resist the constant temptation of
chocolate cake and doughnuts, which seem to appear
magically most days in the common room.

7. Good teeth that need to be exposed when exhibiting that
welcoming smile at the reception desk.

8. Strong cheek muscles to keep the smile there for hours at a
time.

9. A thick skin for withstanding comments of 'the dragon at the door' variety.

10. A computer-quality recall memory to:
    a) Remember the names of all the departments/individuals whom one might need to contact, particularly in an emergency and,
    b) Know the quirks of each individual doctor with regard to their views on being interrupted in the consulting room, being asked to see extra patients in an already overflowing surgery and being pushed generally to the limit.

11. A strong sense of humour.

12. A strong sense of empathy.

Twelve of us have spent a total of 119 years working at the surgery.

'The 'dragon at the gate' label that the doctors' receptionist has acquired is both historical and the inevitable result of acting as the doctor/patient go-between. On the one hand you have the employer who needs his or her workload kept down to a manageable level, and on the other a person whose immediate medical problem is the most important thing in their life. The only obstacle in their direct route to the doctor is the receptionist. It is no wonder that we are viewed by some with dislike. In that moment when the patient is told that the doctor is not immediately available, they feel that the receptionist has not fully understood the depth of their anxiety. Patients do not appreciate that the doctors expect us to filter out the 'immediately necessary' from the 'can wait' and their confidence in us is not improved by the knowledge that we are not medically trained. Certainly they feel happier when told that the decision has been

Dexterity in dealing with a patient on the phone and a doctor by your side.

made after a personal appeal to the doctor. Of course the practicalities of this being applied in every case would result in constant interruption during surgery, which would be most disconcerting for the doctor and patient in the consulting room.

'One of the worst instances of being a go-between, and one all receptionists dread, is that, while you are telling a patient at the desk that their doctor is not working that day, you feel their eyes straying over your shoulder into the eyes of their doctor, who is standing behind you. He or she has just looked in to the surgery to attend to something personal. How to come out of this situation without the word 'liar' imprinted across your forehead takes all the skills that a fast talker can muster.

'It may come as some surprise to a lot of patients to know how fond you can become of them and how difficult it may be not to show some bias towards one patient over another. Our particular favourites are usually mild-mannered elderly gentlemen, slightly eccentric old ladies, local personalities or anyone who shows some genuine appreciation that we are only trying to help and not hinder his or her path to the doctor. Perhaps it would help to be reminded that we are sometimes patients too, and experience the same feelings as them when seeking medical advice for our families or ourselves.

'I originally said that I felt the roots of the "dragon" label were to some extent historical. This stems from remembering the type of

The job of doctor's receptionist is not for the faint-hearted.

receptionist who used to be favoured by doctors in the past. In the case of the one-man practice often the receptionist would be his wife or otherwise the wife of another professional man, working for pin money, or a spinster dedicated to her doctor-employer. This engendered the notion of a receptionist as a barrier because professionalism was unfamiliar to the ordinary man in the street in his dealings with women. In some ways, perhaps, this made the receptionist's job easier, because she had an in-bred confidence which did not invite argument. However, everything changes and modern doctors want their staff to be approachable. Therefore, today's receptionists tend to come from the mainstream educationally and speak the same language as the locals. When I became a receptionist 16 years ago I was one of the first to fall into that latter category, which made me feel rather out of place, but nowadays I feel comfortable working alongside a mixture of the old and new. I believe that there is still a place for the "old style" if it is tempered with some younger people with their more laid-back attitude.

'Going back to that night out with my fellow receptionists, someone asked the question, "Who are receptionists more frightened of, the doctors or the patients?" And that from someone whose job makes her one of the most feared working women in Britain!'

Having read this missive, I considered the points raised and have to admit that it is a pretty accurate picture. I raise my hand as guilty of 'sneaking' off without my messages – not always intentionally, I hasten to add. I must also admit to failing to resist the doughnuts and chocolate cake, as my ever-increasing girth bears witness.

I have always had a weight problem and have, over the years, tried a number of different foolproof diets. The truth of the matter is, I like my food too much. Show me a lettuce leaf and my heart sinks – chocolate cake and now you're talking. The most effective diet I tried was when I was in the RAF. It was a diet sheet produced by the American Airforce and set out all food to be eaten over a given period. By the end of eight weeks I was actually slim and it is hard to believe that I had such a fine profile when I look at photographs at that time. (Pale, wan and unhappy but verifiably slim!) It was also the only time I have ever threatened my poor wife with violence. By week three, I was losing weight nicely, but was completely obsessed with what I was going to eat for the next meal. One evening I came home with the happy knowledge that as I had not had time to eat lunch I would be able to eat lunch and dinner all in one go and therefore have a sensible-sized meal. Now I feel I must point out that I do not usually expect to have my dinner served up for me on my return from work, but when I am unfortunate enough to have agreed to lose some weight, Annie has to take over all catering or I find that I have inadvertently eaten an enjoyable (fattening) meal. On this particular evening, a sparse plate of food was put in front of me. My heart did not sink as usual because I knew that I could also have my lunch allowance.

'I didn't have any lunch today so I can have that now.' All said in a bright and optimistic tone.

'If you miss a meal you can't make it up.' All said in a conversational tone which indicated that the seriousness of the situation had not been recognized.

'I had no lunch so I can have the lunch I should have had now. What was it?' This time bright with a slightly concerned edge to the tone.

After reference being made to the chart on the kitchen wall I was told it was the dreaded lettuce, cucumber and a tomato and vinaigrette salad. In my desperate state it sounded delicious.

'You can't have it. If you miss a meal you can't just add it to the next meal.' A note of steel in the voice.

'Don't be ridiculous. Is it in the fridge?' Knife and fork put down, I turned to face the hard woman who is my wife.

'You can't have it. It specifically says on this chart that you cannot carry on food from one meal to another.'

Usually I am a placid chap. I never can be bothered to get in a state about anything. I'm not a shouter, I never lose my temper – not because I can control it, but because I don't seem to have one – but that evening I looked across at my ever-thin wife as she stood by the wretched chart and I began to get hot and very bothered.

'Just give me the salad and tomatoes.' No niceties – this was war!

She ignored me. I went to the fridge. She barred my way. This was my own personal 'dragon at the door', in this case the fridge door.

'For goodness sake, just let me get the rest of my dinner.'

And then she laughed. I was hungry, weak from three weeks of dieting and in no mood for misplaced humour.

'I'm going to have the tomatoes.' Volume gently turned up to about four.

There was no response, as my eat-anything-and-not-put-on-a-pound wife could not speak for laughing.

' Get out of my way. I'm going to have the tomatoes.' Now at about volume eight.

The scraggy hag had to support herself on the fridge as she became ever more hysterical.

'I want my tomatoes.' Off the volume scale …

Sadly, that story is true and Annie has often (and boringly, in my book) delighted in recalling the day I was eventually to be found screaming at the top of my voice:

'Give me my tomatoes!'

Well, 18 years on I'm still tucking into the chocolate cake, but this year I have set myself perhaps the most public challenge to lose weight ever, in that I've agreed to be weighed weekly, in front of the television cameras.

It all started when Dot finally decided to have her hip replacement. Dot Lupo, who lives with her husband Dan, has had the most difficult of times since she suffered complications after surgery for arthritis of the left hip in 1983. Because of her age and size she was advised, instead of a hip replacement, to have an operation known as an osteotomy, which alters the position of the thigh bone and relieves some of the pressure on the diseased hip joint. Fourteen years ago artificial hip joints were regarded as having a limited life span and the idea was that the osteotomy would be less risky and would leave the way open to hip replacement at some time in the future. Dot had immediate problems post-operatively and the new bone fixation failed to heal properly. She underwent a second operation and had some metalwork put in to support the bone, and six months later she needed yet another bone-grafting operation. It took more than a year for her to get back to anything like full mobility and even then she was limited by back and hip pain. As the years have passed she has gradually suffered increasing pain and her mobility has deteriorated to the point that she can only get around painfully with the aid of elbow crutches. She was advised six years ago to struggle on and avoid further surgery but now, 14 years on, the pain and severely reduced mobility is intolerable. She has seen another orthopaedic surgeon who is willing to go ahead now and she has agreed.

Few of us relish the prospect of going into the operating theatre, and when you have previously had a bad experience with surgery you are even more reluctant. The time is never right and excuses are made as other things take priority. In Dot's case Dan has been unwell for some time, her father who lives in the Midlands has needed her to visit him regularly and she has managed to find other good reasons for postponing the operation. However, Dot has always been everybody's confidante and helper – and not being able to help her friends, not even able to babysit – has been the last straw.

We have discussed the situation many times and I knew, before she came to see me a month ago, that she was ready to go ahead. At that consultation we discussed the matter again and finally she heaved a big sigh and said, 'I can't go on like this any longer, I'm just going to have to face it.' I had made some enquiries with Musgrove

Hospital about the likely date for the operation. Having postponed before, Dot has been at the top of the list for some time and October was suggested as a possible date for admission. This suits her and her other family commitments so it gives her four months to prepare and in particular to lose some weight to reduce her anaesthetic risk. I know how difficult it is for her. When she went for her first operation 14 years ago she was told by her orthopaedic surgeon that he wouldn't do the operation until she had lost at least a stone in weight. She tried hard on her own, but made little progress. In the end, the frustration and failure made it all worse and she actually managed to gain rather than lose weight.

This time I decided that she would have all the support I could lend and, in a sudden rush of blood to the head, I said that I would diet and lose weight with her. That would have been all right if I had kept the idea to myself – I could have conveniently forgotten about it – but I made the cardinal mistake of announcing it while I had a film crew in the consulting room. A psychologist will tell you that it was entirely premeditated – which, of course, is probably the case. Eighteen months ago I did well to lose two stone but it has been creeping slowly back on and I knew that I had to do something about it. I told Dot of my plan and she agreed. What we both needed was motivation and I think I have managed to give both of us that!

We are on a low-fat and therefore low-calorie plan and are weighed at the end of each week – in front of the cameras. I am pleased to report that so far, so good. I am aware of the potential harm if I succeed and Dot fails, so I will take care not to be too successful. (That's my ready-made excuse when I forget to decline an elevenses piece of surgery cake.) And anyway, if Dot starts overtaking me on the weight-loss scene I can always make contact with the American Airforce to find out whether they now allow that extra tomato.

6

ONJ 537

This morning I drove my rusty old Land Rover to the surgery as my trusty old MG was in a temperamental mood and failed to start. She will be all right if I clean her and fill the windscreen washer bag. The only disadvantage with the Land Rover is that the ignition is broken and I have to start it up with a screwdriver. I can't remember a time when I have owned a wholly reliable car and I think it has become a bit of a trademark. Not for me the desire to drive around in a pristine new three-door hatchback. I have been known, in a transportation crisis, to drive the tractor to the surgery – front bucket and link-box still attached – and recently, while bringing the quad bike home after a puncture repair, I combined the trip with a home visit to a patient. A couple of weeks ago, when I had the misfortune to step on a rusty nail in the pigsty, the quad bike was my only choice of transport to the casualty department, as my sore and bleeding foot was incapable of operating the accelerator pedal – or, more importantly, the brake.

As any MG enthusiast knows, the B-type GT model is not exactly spacious in the back seat, and this has led to some interesting problems while filming with the BBC this year. The MGB is not a film crew's dream of a car, and during the making of the television series it has been the cause of some distress to them. Dismissing the idea of attaching a small camera to the glove compartment (apparently the suspension is too hard and the camera would judder with every bump in the road – and anyway the fascia is none too sturdy), the crew reluctantly decided to squeeze themselves into the car. Our first crew was very MG-friendly. The cameraman, Jon, is a tall slim man with the ability to contort his body into any available space like a bendy toy, and he slipped into the passenger seat with great ease, sticking the back end of his large Sony Betacam out through the open window. Keith, the sound recordist, was equally agile and spent many a long journey sprawled neatly across the back parcel shelf. It was like travelling with a 'live' nodding dog.

Jon and Keith sadly left us after the first month of filming to take up an assignment elsewhere and crew number two arrived. The cameraman, Jeremy, was equal in stature to Jon. But then along came Dudley. Now, it's no coincidence that Dudley is known in BBC circles as Cuddly Dudley from Budleigh (he hails from Budleigh Salterton in Devon), and even if I had a top-of-the-range BMW, there was no way that he was going to fit on to the back parcel shelf. Apparently the BBC encourage multi-skilling, which is just as well, as Christine, the slightly built producer, was able and willing to take up the sound recordist role of nodding dog with room to spare, while Dudley was relegated to the crew car following behind.

Now I come to think of it, there is one car that I have owned, ONJ 537, which would have accommodated all three film crews at once, but first you must know a little background history. I was in my final year as a medical student at Charing Cross Hospital Medical School in London. Towards the end of that year, before the last set of exams, the medical school witnessed humiliating scenes of final-year students grovelling for their first payslip. Consultants would be accosted in corridors:

'Please, sir, please, sir, may I be your houseman, sir?' Which really meant, 'May I be your humble servant? May I show suitable contrition when you throw insulting glances or words in my general direction? May I be at your bidding at all hours of the day and night, and please can I work on your private patients without expecting any payment?'

Mr Peter Philip, consultant urologist at Charing Cross Hospital, had a reputation for eating students and theatre staff for lunch as well as breakfast, and he must have breakfasted early because his ward rounds often started at 7 a.m. In order to become fully registered with the General Medical Council, all doctors have to complete a year's pre-registration employment as a house officer – six months in general medicine and six months in surgery.

A split job of three months in urology and three in arterial surgery was available, probably because nobody was expected to survive a full six months with Peter Philip. I had no problem in asking, and being accepted for the first three months by, Mr Bliss, a general and arterial surgeon on the professorial unit. I then went along to Peter Philip's office with great trepidation and was told by his secretary to catch him wherever I could find him. I finally caught up with him and his current entourage on the back stairwell and thought I would try a different tack to show my individualism:

'May I be your houseman, sir?' (On reflection, while I had dropped the 'Please, sir. Please, sir. Three bags full, sir', I rather think the unusually high pitch of my voice let me down.)

'I do not see why not, Slade.' It all seemed so simple, and I skipped home with joy in my heart.

After three months of amputating bloodless limbs and spending five hours holding back livers during aortic operations, I joined Peter Philips' firm. Of course, he did not live up to his reputation. There were a few times when I was subjected to one of his renowned withering glances, but, to my surprise, I got on extremely well with him and had an enjoyable time. I do, though, recall one occasion when I managed to push him beyond his usual silent contempt. Prostate operations had always been done by cutting into the lower abdomen, but a new technique was being developed known as transurethral prostatectomy (TURP), which is now a commonplace procedure. Through a telescope that was introduced through the penis into the bladder, a hot wire loop was drawn backwards, removing slivers of the prostate tissue. This, of course, caused some bleeding and the blood was removed from the field of view by a steady flow of water into the bladder. When the bladder was full, the telescope was removed and the water, with bits of prostate, was drained out. It was the houseman's job to catch the water in a bowl, holding a sieve above it to catch the pieces of tissue. The bowl was then emptied into a bucket by our side.

Peter was beavering away at his operation while I chatted with the rest of the theatre staff, cracking our best and latest jokes. He sat back and I put my bowl and sieve in place. I had just got to the punch line when the bowl filled and, without looking, I emptied its contents into the bucket. Instead of falling about in hysterical laughter, the theatre attendants looked at me with abject horror. I turned around and found that instead of emptying the bloodstained water into the bucket, I had poured it over and into the great man's Wellington boot. Not a word was spoken as he reintroduced the hot wire loop and continued with his operation. At the end of the procedure he stood up, took his gloves and gown off and walked across the operating theatre – step squelch, step squelch. When he got to the door he turned and gave me a look not of deserved contempt but of resigned sympathy. 'Slade, you are a tit.'

A few weeks later when we were working in the out-patient department, quite out of the blue he asked me if I had a car. I had been forced to sell our Triumph Spitfire in order to accommodate a

Not for me the desire to drive a pristine new three-door hatchback.

pram and all the other equipment required for our new baby. We were stony-broke but had found £40 to buy an old Hillman Minx which, although roadworthy, was not particularly reliable and drove like a pig.

'Not really,' I said to him.

'Then you may be pleased to know that my father has decided to give up driving and is looking for a home for his car. Would you like it?'

He told me that it was a Rover 105, a car that I had never really been aware of, but it was in fairly good condition and in appreciation of the help I had given him as an operating assistant, he would be willing to pay half of it for me. It would cost me £75. A quick

calculation told me that I was going to get at least twice the usual rate for three months' private work. While we did not have £75, going without food, clothing and nappies for three weeks should see us through. I readily accepted his kind offer. A week later Peter delivered the car to the car park of the accommodation block where we lived on the tenth floor. Handing me the keys he pointed out where he had parked the car and, refusing the offer of a lift home, walked off into the night. It was dark and pouring with rain so it was not until the following morning that we went down to inspect the new family transport.

It really was the poor man's Rolls-Royce, and in perfect condition! It gleamed; polished both inside and out it was the most magnificent machine. It had a walnut dashboard and the smell of the leather upholstery lent an atmosphere of unadulterated luxury as we entered the car. Even the armrests were adjustable and we sat in the car adjusting and admiring to our hearts' content. The back seat was like a big, comfortable armchair and when we sat on the front bench seat, we were so far apart that we needed megaphones to communicate. The slide-out tool box was complete with all its bits and pieces and we did not need to read the original service record to realize that the car had always been lovingly maintained (down to the door hinges being oiled and that oiling recorded on a weekly basis from new). There were two overdrive switches – one on the steering column and one next to the accelerator in case you could not be bothered to flick your finger. Having investigated the inside, we walked round our new car admiring every aspect of its pristine loveliness. We moved round to the back and, on opening the boot, found that, as well as leaving us this lovely machine, Peter had also left us a bottle of champagne.

ONJ 537 was the family car for many years. We put it into storage for three years while we lived in Germany but put it back on the road when we moved to Somerset. However, by that time we had four children and ONJ was not a very practical car for a growing family. As a practice vehicle it was hopeless, drinking gallons of petrol for the frequent short journeys I was making for my visits – and spare parts were becoming very hard to come by. We decided that ONJ would have to be sold, but for sentimental reasons could never quite get around to taking it to a garage. We needed to find it a good home.

Sir Edward Mallet lived in decaying splendour in his estate house out on the hills. A life-long Rover enthusiast, he had learned to adapt each car to his personal taste. Out came the front bench seat, to be replaced by his favourite armchair. This left him sitting a little low, but he could see ahead by looking between the dashboard and the top of the steering wheel and his feet reached the pedals satisfactorily. The absent front-passenger seating left ample space for any sheep that he wanted to transport and there was room for two more in the back.

I first met him when, quite unaccountably, he had come down a country lane and smacked straight into the front of a bus. I learnt later that, sadly, his car was damaged beyond repair and that this had clearly caused him more regret that his own injuries. He did not really want to call a doctor but was eventually persuaded to seek some medical attention. My partner Philip, his usual doctor, was away and as duty doctor for the day, the task fell upon me.

I arrived at the house, knocked on the door, which was ajar, and, receiving no response, went into the house. I called out and heard a reply from a distant room. Sir Edward was sitting very uncomfortably in a chair with his walking stick beside him. Playing down his symptoms – he was obviously finding it painful to breathe – he insisted that the main purpose of my visit was to accept a large glass of whisky from him. So as not to offend, I accepted the offer, although having regard for my driving licence, not to mention my liver, I later discreetly disposed of the contents. After some minutes chatting I finally persuaded him to remove some clothing and found the most extensive bruising that I had ever seen. Physical examination showed that he had fractured at least two ribs, but his lung fields were clear. I wanted to take him into hospital for pain relief and general care, but he would have none of it. I eventually managed to persuade him to accept a prescription for some decent painkillers and reluctantly took my leave.

Despite my protests Sir Edward insisted on seeing me out of the house and we made slow progress, with the dignified old man hobbling along beside me, clearly in pain. However, when we got to the front door his eyes lit up and he became a changed man. He had seen my Rover 105 and his salvation. He wanted to buy the car there and then. It seemed very appropriate that as I had not been able to do anything very much for him medically, I could at least help solve his transportation problem. Sir Edward took possession of ONJ the following week.

I would see the car occasionally around town and Sir Edward would always raise his hat and give me a friendly toot. Once fully recovered from his injuries, he had set about customizing the car to satisfy both his and his farm's transport needs. It no longer gleamed and the door hinges were undoubtedly strangers to the oil can, but I felt content that a car of character had found a perfect match in Sir Edward.

7

The Cottage Hospital

Today it is my turn for a duty stint in casualty and, as usual, this means a bit of a later start, as although we take on the cover at 8.00 a.m., usually nothing turns up until nine o'clock when the X-ray department opens. Irnham Lodge and our neighbouring Harley House practice give full 24-hour cover for the department and this, together with our other commitments, leads to somewhat complex duty rotas. The doctor who is first on call at night covers the general practice patients for emergency calls as well as casualty. This can lead to problems if, for example, there is an urgent call to a distant rural patient, which would leave casualty uncovered. To get round that problem we always have someone 'second' on call, who has to remain available over the duty period, just in case a 'two-places-at-one-time' situation arises. During the day, normal practice surgeries still have to carry on, so both practices have to spend quite some time plotting the rotas to ensure full cover for their practice and the hospital (and, in our case, the police surgeon's cover). The rota also has to ensure that no doctor is on duty for longer or more often than is safe – both for the doctors' and the patients' health and wellbeing.

If the practices did not cover casualty, then the nearest accident and emergency department would be in Taunton, nearly 30 miles away. Over the years, Minehead has lost some medical services. For example, there used to be maternity beds in our hospital, but now mothers-to-be have to travel to Taunton for hospital delivery and we have had a number of children over the years who have decided they would rather greet the world on the Bishops Lydeard bypass. We support our local community in trying to maintain our medical services and in the best of all worlds we would like Minehead to be even more medically self-sufficient, but, realistically, the cost of the back-up support that would be required is financially prohibitive. The viability of the Minehead casualty department is dependent on our willingness to provide the medical cover and there are times, when we are under particular stress in the practice, when we feel on the verge of giving up the responsibility. However, we know that if the casualty department was ever to be closed down the local

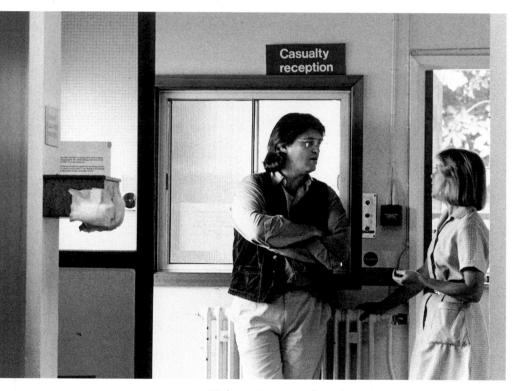

*Today it is my turn for a duty stint
in casualty.*

populace would be justified in having a sense of grievance. To have to travel 30 miles, on the twisting, mostly single-lane A39, to get to the nearest accident and emergency department would be far from ideal and more of the load would fall directly on us in the GP surgeries.

As well as the casualty department, the hospital has many other facilities. The busy out-patient department runs clinics for visiting specialists in most of the medical and surgical disciplines. I enjoy doing my weekly clinical assistant session in the eye clinic with our ophthalmic consultant, John Twomey, but I'm under pressure to give it up. The standard clinical assistant payment is about £55 for the three-hour session and the cost to the practice of employing a half-day locum in the surgery to replace me is £104. Paying £50 a week for the privilege of working in the hospital is not really acceptable.

Given Minehead's high retired and elderly population, the benefit of admitting our patients on to the in-patient wards at the hospital, whether it is for a short period to nurse and sort out acute illness, for convalescent care from Musgrove or for terminal care, cannot be

The local community benefits enormously from the services offered by Minehead Hospital

overstated. Without these beds, patients and their often elderly relatives would have to travel to Taunton. As with all the services the hospital is able to offer, it means that we are able to try to ensure that there is a minimum of disruption, and that can go a long way towards easing the way to recovery both for patients and relatives. Caring and worrying when someone you love is unwell is bad enough, but the time and expense of a long journey to see them must only add to the burden.

This morning, when I arrive at nine o'clock, I find that there are two patients in the waiting room and two more are on their way down from Butlin's. They have all been seen during the previous evening and night and have been asked to return for review in the morning. Unless we need an X-ray for immediate diagnosis we are reluctant to call the radiographers out after normal working hours. Gill and Jane between them cover the radiology department for 365 days a year and they need to know that they are only going to be called out for genuine emergencies. Gill lives on a hill farm, high up on the moors (where she raises pure-bred Exmoor ponies) and we are not going to get her in unnecessarily. Jane gets the same protection. Most minor undisplaced fractures will come to no harm if supported properly and treated with painkillers, and an X-ray to confirm or exclude a diagnosis can usually wait until morning. Our patients are quite happy to accept this if it is explained clearly to them at the time of their first attendance.

The first patient is a young man with a painful swelling on the side of his right hand. He had come in late last evening saying that he had inadvertently punched a wall. It looks as though he has fractured a bone on the inside of his palm – an injury typical of a closing-time fracas, which I strongly suspect. I ask him how the other bloke is.

'OK ... unfortunately,' he replies, with an air of disappointment.

I fill in the X-ray form and send him through.

The second patient also has a possible fracture – this time it is an ankle injury. A woman in her early fifties, she slipped and fell on her own front doorstep last evening and had been brought in by her husband. She had had an ice-pack applied for 20 minutes by the nurse, who had then put on a supporting elastic bandage. With advice to continue the cooling therapy by using a packet of frozen peas at home, she was asked to attend for review this morning. The outer side of the ankle is fairly swollen and there is a little bruising appearing below the ankle bone. I press, firmly but gently, over the points of the ankle and outer part of the foot which is where fractures, if there are any, are most likely to be. She is not showing any clinical sign of fracture and the outer ankle ligament is very tender, indicating a sprain.

X-rays in themselves are not without risk and we have to make a balanced judgement in each case whether or not to use them to make a diagnosis. They are also expensive: each ankle X-ray, for example, costs around £40 and if I order only a dozen unnecessary pictures a

We need to plan the mixture of home and hospital care for Tom.

year I am wasting a considerable amount of valuable money for the NHS. On the other hand, if every ankle injury is not X-rayed the occasional fracture will be missed. In this case I decide that a fracture is unlikely and I explain this to the patient. If she is not making a suitable recovery in a few days she will return for a second opinion.

Meanwhile, she is given a strong elastic support and some written instructions on the dos and don'ts of exercise.

The Butlin's patients have not arrived yet, so I am able to go up to the wards to check on my in-patients – I have two male patients in the upstairs ward at the moment and one elderly lady on the female ward downstairs – and to call in at the day hospital.

The most recent major development at Minehead Hospital was the transfer of the geriatric day hospital on to the main site and the expansion of the occupational therapy department. The day hospital was formerly at Irnham Lodge and the move enabled us to buy the old building for our new surgery premises. Simon Cooper, our new consultant in what we prefer to call 'elderly medicine' is a congenial sort who, like me, tends to take his work, but not himself, seriously. When policemen start looking too young you know you are getting older, but when it starts happening with consultants you know it's time to start thinking seriously about retirement! Having the ability to look into out-patients or the day hospital to discuss an awkward problem with a consultant or to make an appeal on behalf of a patient is very useful, and I have come to see Simon today to discuss a mutual patient. Tom suffers from a form of pre-senile dementia and Simon has seen him recently. Simon and I need to discuss the implications of the results of Tom's blood tests and we need to plan the mixture of home care and hospital care that we can provide. Tom's wife wants him at home as much as possible and we will do our utmost to facilitate that. Being a caring man, Simon invites me back for coffee later when he has a break. The hospital kitchens at Minehead must be some of the best in the NHS – none of this cook-chill nonsense here – and I'm sure it is their home-made Viennese whirls that encourage all the visiting consultants to keep coming!

I continue on to the wards and, after checking in with the nurses, I see Jim who, in his late eighties, is diabetic and was admitted by the duty doctor six days ago with a bout of pneumonia. In general, his health is not too bad, but he and his wife, who is crippled with arthritis, are finding it increasingly difficult to run their home without a lot of help from friends and neighbours – only recently a neighbour stopped me in the street to tell me how much trouble they are having. The district nurses spend a great deal of their time looking after Jim and Ethel and I have talked to them both before about the possibility of their needing some sort of sheltered accommodation. Ethel has been reluctant until now to think about moving but these few days, while Jim has been in hospital, have caused her to reconsider and now she is very keen. His family have been down from the Midlands over the weekend and they have obviously had a long talk about it. We have some very good 'part three' sheltered accommodation in the area in which the residents have their independence and freedom, but where help is directly on hand should they need it. 'Part three' housing is run by the district council and administered by Social Services. A social worker has been allocated to them and will see them both in the next two days to start the ball rolling. There are no places available at the moment and we have no idea how long they will wait, but at least the decision is made.

My other male patient has just returned from Musgrove Hospital after a prolonged stay. Nick is 58 years old and had a stroke five years ago, followed by the onset of epilepsy. He made a slow, but eventually good, recovery and was left only with a weakness in his right hand. Three months ago he sadly suffered a second brain haemorrhage and has been having intensive physiotherapy, but his right-sided weakness is showing no sign of improvement and his progress has ground to a halt. Nick is totally unable to look after himself and there is no one in his family able to care for him physically. He will need long-term nursing-home care and the first hurdle to get over is his acceptance of the fact. One of the residual problems of his stroke is that his powers of reasoning are not recovered and he cannot really understand his situation or the options open to him. The ward nurses and occupational therapists have spent a lot of time with him, but he does not really comprehend his difficulties and has what are, sadly, unreasonable expectations for his future. It is very hard for him. We will continue to try and persuade him to accept a place at a local nursing home and, meantime, his social worker will look into the funding side of things.

While I am talking to Nick a message comes that the X-rays are back and the Butlin's patients have arrived – so back to casualty.

The young man's hand is fractured, but there is no great displacement of the metacarpal bone and it will heal perfectly satisfactorily. A boxing-glove bandage will protect the injury and we will check him again in the fracture clinic in 10 days' time.

One of the patients from Butlin's is presenting the same problem as my second patient of the day. This lady fell on the dance floor last night, twisting her ankle, and had hobbled back to her accommodation. This morning, unable to stand and take any weight on her foot, she thought she should get it checked. She saw the doctor in the medical centre, who sent her up to casualty. This time there is tenderness over the ankle bone and I order an X-ray. The other patient is a girl of 10 who fell from a slide onto her arm. The lower forearm is tight and tender and she doesn't like rotating the wrist. It looks like a greenstick fracture and, again, I order an X-ray.

While I am writing up my notes and filling in the X-ray forms a man in white working overalls comes to the reception hatch. Fishermen caught with their own hooks, butchers with cut fingers, welders with arc-eye are all meat and drink to the casualty doctor, and here's another one: the carpenter with a splinter. Carpenters are very resourceful with splinters and most have their favourite chisel or bradawl for digging them out, but he hasn't even tried with this one. If it had been my finger I would have been prostrate on the floor. A two-inch spear of wood had ripped up underneath the nail of his index finger, splinting the top joint so that he could not bend it. Horrid for him, but ideal for me. It's the little ones that are more difficult to remove, or the ones that have been left too long and fall to bits every time you get hold of them. An anaesthetic injection around the base of the finger freezes the whole digit within a couple of minutes and the splinter comes out quite easily with a pair of splinter forceps. Some prophylactic antibiotics to prevent any possibility of infection, a check that his last tetanus is in date and a bandage to keep the wound clean (and big enough for sympathy's sake) and he is straight back to work.

By the time the splinter is out the next set of X-rays is back. The ankle picture is difficult to read: there is some arthritis in the joint and some changes showing over the tip of the bone in which I was suspecting a flake fracture. I take the pictures to the radiologist's viewing room and use the bright light to look more carefully: there is a fracture, but the edges are smooth and this looks like an old injury. The patient denies having broken it before, but I can see that she has. There is no sign of a new fracture, but I think this sprain may stir up her arthritis and give her trouble for a while and she is likely to need physiotherapy. She is going home in two days' time so I arrange for her to take the X-rays with her for further follow-up with her own doctor, and prescribe some painkillers.

The 10-year-old's X-ray reveals a greenstick fracture – shown by the kink in one of the forearm bones near the wrist. When we are young our bones are relatively soft and instead of snapping when put under pressure they tend to bend and then go back into shape. The greenstick is a good description. These sorts of fractures do not distort the bone to any degree and simple immobilization with a strengthened plaster bandage gives good pain relief. I explain all this to her and her mother. The casualty nurses are all trained to apply various plaster and fibreglass casts and Karen, who is on duty today, will put it on. The plaster will need to be worn for about three weeks so, like the last patient, she will need follow-up at home. We always check a plaster 24 hours after it has been applied to make sure that it has not become too tight, so when she and her mother come back tomorrow we will give them the X-rays to take home.

Iris is the sister in charge of the casualty department and we rely on her as much as she relies on us. A lot of the patients that come to casualty have minor injuries and problems that really don't need the attention of a doctor. Many people pop in for a bit of advice or just to check that they're correct in not seeking medical assistance. Iris and her experienced staff will filter cases and, of course, if in any doubt will call the duty doctor for telephone advice or a visit. I have recently had personal experience of the service they offer when I had the misfortune to tread on a rusty nail whilst tending to my pigs – it went straight through my boot and very nearly reappeared through the top of my foot. It was an interesting and comforting experience to be on the receiving end of Iris's tender ministrations.

Following my trip to casualty I was in much disfavour with Christine, the producer of the BBC documentary, as the event was not caught on film. It simply hadn't occurred to me to alert the film crew to my own medical emergency – I was too busy being alerted to the intense pain I was feeling at the time! A few weeks later, and still feeling guilty, I was on duty in casualty when I received a message on my bleep – 'Huw Thomas – nail through thumb – arriving in casualty shortly' – joy of joys! He must have been playing about with his boat again and injured himself. Huwie could be the 'patient' on film, Christine would be happy, and my guilt allayed. I picked up the phone and dialled.

'You'd better get down here straight away, Huwie's on his way to the hospital with a nail through his thumb.'

'Great, we're on our way.' Sympathetic lot, aren't we?

Five minutes later, the crew arrived in casualty, but there was still no sign of Huwie. Good, we could catch him unawares as he arrived. Several minutes passed and we ran through the possibilities of it being a hoax call, or even a practical joke on Huw's part. As the minutes ticked away with still no Huwie, we were sure that must be the case. The crew began to pack up their equipment as we marvelled at Huwie's ingenuity. At that moment, a middle-aged man came through the casualty doors with his wife and I overheard him give his name to the receptionist.

'Hugh Thomas,' he announced.

I looked at Christine, she looked at me, and we both began to laugh. We hadn't even considered the possibility that there could be another Hugh Thomas in Minehead. We quickly explained our mirth to the couple who were quite reasonably bemused by our reaction to their arrival at the hospital. Thankfully, they thought it was funny, too, and joined in the joke. I led Mr Thomas through to one of the casualty bays to deal with his injury while his wife chatted about the marvellous BBC coverage of Ascot to the film crew.

It wasn't until they left that I discovered Mrs Thomas's worries about the incident. Halfway through my consultation with her husband, she had turned to the producer and asked, 'When is the doctor arriving?'

'That's him in there with your husband.'

'Oh, thank goodness,' she said. 'I thought he was your cameraman.'

I have never been mistaken for a cameraman before, and Mrs Thomas must have wondered what on earth I was doing ministering to her husband's thumb. There have, however, been other occasions when the patient has not believed I am a doctor. Just the other morning I went out to visit a patient of Tim's who I had not met before. It was pouring with rain and I was wearing an old anorak that I'd found in the back of the MG. I was greeted at the front door with, 'Two pints please. Sorry I can't stop for a chat, I'm waiting for the doctor.'

Back to this morning and, a few cuts and bruises later, the waiting room is empty and I can get away for some GP work. I have recently discharged a patient from the hospital and I want to check on his progress at home.

Stanley, a retired headmaster, needed emergency surgery two years ago for a bowel obstruction and, during an exploratory operation, the surgeon's suspicion of bowel cancer was confirmed. The tumour was removed and although it was fairly large, it looked as though all the growth had been excised and there was no sign of further spread. He was well until eight weeks ago when he suffered a second obstruction. His cancer had recurred and, sadly, this time it was not possible to operate to remove it. Stan came back to Minehead Hospital in a poor condition and I was not expecting him to survive

Butchers with cut fingers, welders with arc-eye and carpenters with splinters are all meat and drink to the casualty doctor.

for long. However, his strong spirit, together with excellent nursing care, has meant that as the days passed he gradually improved. His post-operative chest and wound infections cleared, and he started eating more. Three weeks later, after checking with Chris Rogers, our senior district nurse, that she and her team could manage, I was able to say to him, 'What do you think about going home?'

'If you think it is possible.' He really hadn't expected to see his own home again and he was clearly surprised by the suggestion. Iris, his dear wife, was a little hesitant as to whether she would be able to cope, but, after speaking to Chris about the support she would have, she was reassured and we went ahead with the plans. We had a hospital bed installed by the window in their dining room, giving him a view across the valley and now I want to check that all is going well.

Bearing in mind his condition Stan looks terrific. The move was tiring, but he is getting over it now. He is spending some time on some paperwork and getting some of his affairs sorted out. Iris is fantastic – she is a natural nurse and is coping during the day with all the routine care and has the help of a district nurse who visits twice a day. However, she is finding nights hard and I see that she has a put-u-up bed for herself in the dining room. She can't bear to leave Stan downstairs while she is sleeping upstairs. She knows that if she leaves him alone she will spend all night awake listening out for every sound. She sleeps soundly in a bed on the floor next to him. A nurse who will stay overnight is being arranged so that she can have a break.

I check through Stan's tablets and see that he has the supplies that he needs. He is not experiencing any particular pain – 'more restlessness than anything else' he tells me – but he is getting nauseous and I adjust the medications. I will get a blood check done. If this goes on for any length of time I expect that he will become anaemic, in which case I will take him back into hospital for a couple of days for a transfusion. We have a chat and, as I move to leave, he takes my hand and in his gentle manner thanks me for all I've done. I have done very little really – I stand in the middle while Iris, the nurses, and others do all the work – and I tell him so. His smile and firming up of the handshake will encourage me to stand around for him as much as I can.

On the way back to the surgery my bleep goes off again for casualty. A patient is on her way in by ambulance following a fall. I arrive before the ambulance, so Iris and I have the coffee that I should have had earlier with Simon. My eldest son Ben and Iris's son Eddy are both in different parts of Australia, discovering that country (and themselves) before college, and we are able to comfort each other about the lack of contact we have with our offspring.

The ambulance arrives with an old lady who has been pulled over by her dog. If we fall forwards our natural tendency is to put our hand out to save ourselves and as a result we see a large number of Colles' fractures each year, in which the wrist is broken and forced backwards. It is best when tripping forwards to try and roll into the fall, in best paratrooper fashion – but please don't complain to me if you dislocate your shoulder instead!

This lady's wrist is well and truly gone and the deformity is an obvious Colles' fracture. I order an X-ray to see the full extent of the injury and explain to her that I will need to re-set it. If it is left in its current position it will heal, but she will have a residual deformity that will cause her difficulty with her grip. After the X-ray is done I explain what I need to do and, after getting her written consent to the procedure, I draw the curtains around to make the atmosphere as quiet as possible and insert an intravenous line.

We use an intravenous painkiller and a sedative to re-set wrist fractures. It is not a true anaesthetic as the patient is not unconscious, but she will relax and sleep through the process. The other great advantage is that the sedative causes amnesia, and it is not uncommon, even if the patient has reacted to the manipulation of the fracture with a groan, for them to ask afterwards whether the job has been done yet. In this case, being elderly, she does not require too much sedative before her jaw drops and she is lightly snoring.

Gill is the duty radiographer today and we must have pulled and manipulated a hundred Colles' fractures together over the years. After declining the offer of protective aprons – we know that Debbie the staff nurse is a tidy plasterer – we get into our positions. Gill takes the top end of the arm and I take the business end and, putting our feet together so that we don't slip, we apply the traction. The click as the broken ends of the bone move back into position is most satisfying and we nod acknowledgement to each other. I hold the wrist in its new position while Debbie applies the plaster, and a few minutes later, after the plaster-of-paris has begun to dry, we take the patient through for a check X-ray. All is well and as we take her back to the casualty department she is waking up – and asking if we've done it yet! After two hours' recuperation and a cup of tea she will be ready for home. (Should my advice be taken, regarding a 'rolling' fall, Gill and I do a nice line in dislocated shoulders as well!)

Wrist set, notes written up, my duty stint comes to an end and I hand over to my colleague. I bid farewell to Iris and head off back to the surgery for the weekly, lunch-time practice meeting.

As I head for the car in front of the hospital I see a patient, Minty Nixon, across the road. I have been seeing her regularly over the last few years due to a problem she's suffering with her kidneys. As a hard-working hairdresser her priorities are always to her customers and I know she finds it difficult taking the time off for an appointment with me. A consultation outside Kwiksave saves both her time and mine and I am able to give her the test results she's been waiting for.

Some days it's best to keep your head down and avoid eye contact altogether or you find your half-hour shopping expedition has turned into an impromptu surgery in public. Driving through the streets is just as bad, and my hands frequently leave the wheel to acknowledge passing patients who recognize me by my muddy, maroon MG. A few months ago, I was in the middle of my weekly eye clinic at the hospital and popped out to fetch some records from the surgery. On my way I was so intent on averting my eyes from waving passers-by that I missed my own son, Oliver, who was standing at the side of the road madly flapping his arms to attract my attention for a lift home. In fact, my family are constantly berating me for failing to return a friendly smile.

By far the most frustrating and difficult place to meet your patients is the supermarket. They greet you when your mind is firmly on the shopping list and attempt to continue their consultations somewhere between the frozen peas and the cling peaches. Of course I know their faces – they are my patients, after all – but what on earth is their name and what did they come to see me about?

'Just wondered if you got my results through, Doc?' enquired an elderly chap while I was ordering some honey-roast at the deli counter. Should I be honest and ask him who he is? Better not upset him.

'Not back yet,' I blurted, quickly turning my attention to the rows of assorted meats and cheeses. He anxiously continued.

'But do you think I need the operation?'

His wife was hovering at his side with a troubled expression on her face. Now get out of this one, Slade.

'I'm afraid I won't know until I've seen the results. I'll call you when they arrive.'

They walked off with a despondent air and I overheard his wife whisper to him, 'Such a nice doctor. I'm surprised he remembered us, he must see so many different people each day.'

Shortly after the birth of my first grandson I was desperate to show Jakey off in public and an excursion to Somerfields suddenly seemed very appealing. For once, I wouldn't mind having the shopping interrupted in order to try out my new proud-grandfather routine. As luck would have it, there wasn't a familiar face in sight and I had to complete three circuits of the car park before an opportunity arose to stop and show him off.

8

The Move to Irnham Lodge

We had a party last week to say goodbye to our registrar Chris Salway, and as I looked around the room I counted more than 50 staff and practitioners. The party was arranged at short notice and a number of people had not been able to attend, but it still brought home the extent to which the surgery establishment has increased in the last few years.

When I moved to Minehead with my family 15 years ago I joined the partnership as an additional doctor. The two GP surgeries in the town had together taken on the running of the casualty department at Minehead Hospital, and each practice had appointed an extra doctor, myself at King Edward Road and Alan Nelson at the Parkhouse Road Surgery. The practice had only just moved out of a temporary building, which, with its green-and-white striped sun awning, looked more like an ice-cream parlour that had escaped from the sea front. We were four doctors with half-a-dozen support staff and two district nurses who also doubled as midwives. The new single-storey building had been designed with an eye to the future and had been wired ready for the coming of the computerized doctor's surgery. We had separate examination rooms, a coffee room, a consulting room as well as a treatment room for the nurses, and room for a pram park outside. We had an ample waiting room with plenty of space for the obligatory fish-tank and we proudly rattled around in our palatial new purpose-built home.

Over the next few years we gradually developed the practice. First, we became a training practice for new GPs and then we took on our own full-time practice nurse. Both needed their own accommodation. With the gradual increase of the numbers of registered patients we found that we needed more office staff. The computers then arrived, and yet more staff to operate them. The first to go was the pram park, which was roofed-in and then incorporated into the waiting room. As the practice grew, the administration grew with it and we appointed a full-time practice manager – bang went the coffee room. Next, the health visitor needed somewhere permanent and an examination room was converted to become her

This was our only chance to build a surgery just as we wanted.

office and treatment room. How we managed all those baby vaccinations in a room little bigger than the broom cupboard with patients queuing in the corridor, I shall never know. Finally, it was proposed that the broom cupboard be turned into extra office space. That, together with the fact that by this time we had become more and more committed to working alongside a number of complementary practitioners and were very keen to develop that partnership, meant we knew we had to find somewhere else to work.

It took us two years to find a suitable site into which to move. We flirted briefly with a house conversion over the road, and a talented local architect, Louise Crossman, drew some clever plans to give us a second floor standing on four steel legs in the middle of our existing building. But neither of these ideas was going to accommodate the practice in the long term. Just as we had grown over the years, Minehead Hospital was undergoing extension and development, and the day hospital for the elderly at Irnham Lodge was incorporated into a new building on the main hospital site. Situated near the centre of town, the large house of Irnham Lodge, with its gardens and outbuildings, was ideal for us and we started making our plans.

Our main constraint, as in all building development, was money. Most general practitioners are self-employed doctors who contract the main part of their working time to the NHS. We are paid under a ridiculously complicated system, which includes various payments for work done and reimbursement of allowable expenses. One of the expenses allowed is for the provision of premises so that we have somewhere to provide general medical services to our registered NHS patients. In the 1970s the state of many GP surgeries was pretty parlous, and for some years GPs have been able to improve their premises under a fairly generous funding scheme known as 'cost-rent'. Under this arrangement, within very strict guidelines dependent on the number of practising partners, the Health Service effectively rents the building from the doctors for a figure that relates to the actual cost of the building. About a year before our move the Somerset Health Authority had decided not to authorize any new cost-rent schemes, but to change to a mixture of improvement grants and 'market' rents. We had managed to miss the boat and had to find other sources of finance. Using the back of the best envelope I could find, I made the calculations. With the grant available, rents from the surgery and a pharmacy, plus a little from the complementary centre, we could afford a £500,000 loan from the bank. A half-a-million-quid loan? The last surgery cost us £90,000 and we thought we were pushing the boat out then. I tried another envelope. The figures didn't change at all. We had long and meaningful discussions around the possibility of decline into penury, then bought some hard hats and decided to take the plunge.

It is a very strange thing that when you want to buy a publicly owned building, the district valuer puts a ridiculously high price on it. Later, when you need to have the same building valued for the purposes of rental income, he will manage to use exactly the same criteria to set the lowest possible figure he can come up with. However, using my best negotiating skills, we agreed on a price with the Health Authority, signed on the dotted line and bought the building.

Moving to a large new building gave us the opportunity to put into practice our wish to forge closer links with the complementary practice of medicine. We had already been in discussion with Tim Jay, a chiropractor whom many of our patients were travelling miles to see in Taunton. He had an excellent reputation and had been working on a research project with the orthopaedic team at Musgrove Hospital. We had wanted him to be able to see our patients in the old surgery, but we simply didn't have the space. We also knew that there were other well-established complementary practitioners in the area, seeing patients in their own homes, and all working in

Huw is very pleased with his 'double aspect' consulting room.

relative isolation. I approached several of them to find out if they would be interested in setting up in a centre dedicated to complementary medicine where they could all work together and share facilities. The response was very positive and we soon had interest from the fields of homeopathy, acupuncture, chiropractic and aromatherapy. We also wanted to be able to accommodate our own physiotherapist, and knew that it would not be long before we needed space for an in-house counselling service. We wanted to have a pharmacy and chemist shop on site, and the old stable building seemed an ideal site for conversion.

Of course, we also had plenty of thoughts about how we wished to design the layout of the GP surgery. It was wonderful to have a blank piece of paper, representing the Irnham Lodge garden, and to be able to sketch out exactly what we wanted. A feature of the old surgery was that the consulting rooms were all wrapped around the central waiting room, with a connecting corridor for privacy and sound insulation. We don't go in for bells and buzzers, preferring to collect our patients individually from the waiting room. This provides a personal touch. It enables us to keep an eye on the waiting room and to gauge the progress of the surgery. The surgery list on the computer screen in the consulting room may tell you who has arrived, but it is not quite the same as being able to see the patients in the waiting room. We are also able to nod an acknowledgement to patients who are waiting, particularly to let them know they have not been forgotten if the surgery is running late. It gets us out of our chairs as well. As officer-in-charge of moving, I managed to allocate myself the room nearest the waiting-room door. Huwie, being the youngest and fittest at the time, has the furthest to go, and I calculate that he covers a good half a mile every week collecting his patients. The concession he gained was to have an extra window put in his corner room, and he is very pleased with his 'double aspect'. We made plenty of provision for the practice nurses – two consulting and treatment rooms, a sluice room for cleaning, and plenty of storage – and the health visitor was allocated an office for consulting as well as a large treatment room.

As the plans developed they became more grandiose. Inspired by a weekend in Versailles I suggested that we should make space for a garden with fountains. I couldn't see how to include a replica of *La galerie des glaces*, but what about a restaurant or coffee shop? My ambitions of looking out of my consulting-room window on to an army of gardeners trimming the formal hedging was reduced in the end to a raised flower bed with a small fountain and waterfall, but the coffee-shop idea was not so ridiculous.

The floor area of the new surgery was being dictated by the local authority rules for the provision of car-parking space. We had provided for ample room in the waiting and reception area, but it had to be trimmed. We also realized that a lot of people would be visiting the building, not only for the GP surgery but also for the complementary centre and the chemist shop. We have a large number of elderly patients who are often brought to the surgery by relatives and friends, and we knew it would be a popular move to provide more than a few chairs for comfort, and dog-eared back copies of *National Geographic* magazine to pass the time.

We must have driven our architects and builders to distraction during the 12 months of the construction, but this was (I hope) our one and only chance to build a surgery just as we wanted it and we needed to be totally involved. It all seemed to take ages at the beginning of the project and I doubted whether we would make the completion date of 1 April 1995, but as Easter approached, everything came together and next we were holding our grand opening. Through Phillip Leech, a former partner now at the Department of Health, we invited the Chief Medical Officer, Dr Kenneth Calman, to say a few kind words and cut the requisite

The new surgery is a pleasant place in which to work.

ribbon, and he duly obliged. Our local MP Tom King turned out, along with other dignitaries bearing badges of office, and to keep up the tradition Sheila baked a cake. All in all a splendid day.

The physical move from the old building to the new had yet again demonstrated the true spirit of the surgery and its staff. The move had to take place between closing King Edward Road at 1.00 p.m. on Saturday and opening at Irnham lodge first thing Monday morning. Transferring 6000 sets of medical records and keeping them all in the correct order was just one of the tasks to which the receptionists set themselves with resolve and good humour, and by Sunday afternoon we were ready for business. It was not only the fact that everyone mucked in and helped that was so impressive, but the very tangible, shared sense of urgency, together with an undeniable excitement that seemed to epitomize the joint-enterprise approach that is taken by our support staff. We were all too well aware that the development and the move itself would not have been so stress-free without all the help, and so, after the move, on the understanding that we would be sent postcards and be allowed to see the holiday snaps, we gave all the staff travel gift vouchers as a reward for their equanimity and patience.

The new surgery is a pleasant place in which to work. It is light and airy and the sound of running water from 'Paul's folly' has a calming effect on all but elderly bladders. Soon after we opened we were pleased to find that we had been included in a Department of Health review that illustrates 'best practice' in surgery design. Our inclusion of the coffee shop and pharmacy and the integration with the complementary practice has been of interest to other doctors from all over the country, many of whom have visited and asked our advice over similar developments.

The coffee shop was an immediate success and greatly appreciated by all those attending the centre, and others who were merely passing on their way to the shops or on their way home from the school run. At the early stage of planning I had made contact with a patient with experience of running her own restaurant. Charlie Hosegood had given up her own establishment because of her young family and I was pleased when she agreed to set up the coffee shop and run it for the first year or so. It was her that came up with the name The Spoonful of Sugar, not, of course, to encourage dental decay, but to help the medicine go down. The Spoonful of Sugar was not conceived as a refreshment counter selling drinks from polystyrene cups and the odd bar of chocolate wafer biscuit. The emphasis was on quality of service and atmosphere and, of course, on good, healthy home-made foods. I don't want to give the idea that I spent hours of my time becoming a part-time restaurateur. I had more than enough to do with the ever-increasing workload in the surgery, so Charlie and I discussed the general plans; she was then given a budget and left to get on with it. She did extremely well, and her success led to an interesting diversion.

On the opposite side of the road from Irnham Lodge there is a church, and Charlie was asked, on a couple of occasions, to open The Spoonful of Sugar for private functions – once for a small wedding reception and on another occasion for a christening party. She was quite happy to do the functions but was unable to sell the essential champagne. What we required was a table licence to sell wines and beers with a meal. Charlie needed to make an application before the local magistrates and, as owner of the establishment, it was appropriate that my name was on the licence as well, so I discussed it with our solicitor to find out about the responsibilities involved. I rather liked the idea of being a licensee and agreed to go to court, thinking that it would take no longer than an hour out of morning surgery. It would have done if a local newspaper reporter had not written a small piece in the *Western Daily Press* along the lines of 'GP becomes pub landlord'. The phone started ringing the same morning with enquiries from the national newspapers and the medical press and over the next few days I ended up doing several live radio interviews. I even had a call from a medical newspaper in New York. We featured on the lunch-time national TV news and some poor man was dragged out to sit in front of a picture of the Houses of Parliament to pontificate about the dangers of medical men encouraging alcohol abuse. Of course we were doing nothing of the sort. We were not setting up a 'tap and barrel' snug in the corner of the waiting room and I had no plans to install optics behind the reception hatch. Luckily, at the same time, a piece in one of the eminent medical magazines reported on the beneficial properties of a daily glass of red wine, and I was quite rightly able to claim the support of my colleagues. As a devotee of Radio 4's *News Quiz* programme I was proud, when driving home after surgery one evening, to hear myself being featured.

Now, two years on, the dust has settled and we are well and truly established in our new home. Charlie, having completed her setting up, has passed over the running of The Spoonful of Sugar and the licence with it and, disappointingly, my name no longer features above the door. The complementary centre goes from strength to strength and now has 22 practitioners working from 10 consulting rooms, and we constantly get approving comments from temporary visiting patients who find that we have the convenience of an attached pharmacy – our own patients are quite used to it now.

When I look back to the early days of the King Edward Road surgery I feel some nostalgia for the quieter life, but the increasing load on general practice has forced us to respond. If I sound a touch self-satisfied, I apologize, but to have been given the opportunity to reorganize the surgery completely, to put into practice so many schemes and dreams is very gratifying.

9

Leather on Willow

Minehead is situated by the sea and has had an active harbour for several centuries, at first as a port for the wool trade to Wales and a centre for the local fishing industry, and more recently for leisure sailing and watersports. The RNLI lifeboat station was established in 1901, and for all the years I have been here doctors in the town have been actively involved as lifeboat crew members. Unfortunately, my superiorly sensitive vestibular apparatus prevents me from being personally involved. That means I get seasick too easily, and I don't like getting my feet wet. The only time I have ever been in a lifeboat was when, as a young RAF officer, I was heaved over the side off the Norfolk coast to be winched up in a helicopter. We often see the local crew playing the same game opposite the farm on a Sunday training sortie and, while it looks like fun, memories of my own experience (much of which was spent bent over the side of the boat) means I know not to volunteer. The one regular contact I do have with the lifeboat is to turn out each year, in my increasingly tight long white trousers, to play a game of cricket. Nowadays the sole purpose of the game is to make the lifeboat crew feel good by allowing them to beat us soundly, but in the past the motivation was even more altruistic.

The tradition was started some 15 years ago by one of our former partners Phillip Leech, who is now a medical adviser at the Department of Health, and Bryan Stoner. Bryan is the husband of one of our practice nurses, Jenny, and was a partner in the neighbouring practice. Both Phil and Bryan were members of the lifeboat crew and when the emergency maroon went up, followed by the loud explosion (this was before the days of the ubiquitous bleeper), both were to be seen rushing from their surgeries in an attempt to arrive first and get a place on the inflatable boat. The RNLI is a remarkable institution, dependent on volunteers willing to drop everything as soon as the call is heard. Of course the crews enjoy what they do but I much admire their continued enthusiasm, especially when it is cold and the winter sea is far from inviting. As with all crewmen, when the call came Phil had to respond immediately. The remaining doctors had to take over his surgery list and patients had to be very patient as their appointment times went out of the door along with their doctor. The same thing was happening in the town at the local butcher's, baker's and candlestick maker's – something that is sometimes taken for granted, but is so vital in a coastal town.

It was Bryan who made the suggestion to the 'Duphalac Man' that his company should sponsor the lifeboat versus doctors' cricket match, and he readily agreed. Drug representatives have a difficult life – a doctor's time is precious and the thought of having to listen to a drug rep extolling the virtues of his product often leads to a negative response to an invitation to discuss the latest wonder-drug on offer. Drug companies used to spend enormous sums of money entertaining doctors in the hope that their slide-show at the end of the evening would influence prescribing practice. When I first joined the practice drug companies regularly tried to arrange nights out at a choice restaurant, in the hope that we would favour their products. However, we were generally uncomfortable about the idea of accepting such generous hospitality and we decided not to accept the enticing invitations to wine and dine at the expense of any drug company. In the case of the cricket match, the arrangement was that the makers of Duphalac – a fine constipatory remedy – would donate £1 for each run made by the medical team and £5 for each lifeboat wicket taken, the proceeds to be donated to RNLI funds. (The Duphalac Man turned up with cratefuls of cider and Jenny Stoner did a nice line in curried stuffed eggs.) As is usual in the local friendly weekday matches, both teams bowl 20 overs, with every player except the wicket-keepers bowling two overs each.

Given that at this time our practice and the neighbouring practice had eight doctors between them, we were a few 'men' short. Phil's wife Nina was a partner and played a canny game. Having witnessed her bowling, there was much reason for remembering that it was a woman who developed the first overarm bowling style. The rest of the team was made up of any of our children old enough to stand and hold a bat and any retired local doctor still able to stand and lean on their bat. I have to admit we were, and are, truly awful. Lack of practice is not really a sufficient excuse for the total lack of hand and eye co-ordination and I recall somewhat sadly that the first year I played all my family turned out to watch. My wife gathered the four children to watch as I took the crease and it was with great pride that I faced the first ball as Annie could be heard saying, 'Look, Daddy's batting, watch Daddy hit the ball and run.'

It was an enjoyable evening and yet again this year we were soundly beaten.

I was, of course, out for a golden duck – another nail in my all-knowing, all-powerful father image, but I was not alone in putting up such a poor show, and the rest of our team fared little better. Things haven't improved much since then. At most we make 120 runs with the lifeboat doing their best to bowl dolly balls so that we can score well. We rarely take any wickets, even if they hit us easy catches. It was and is an enjoyable evening and I can record that yet again, this year we were soundly beaten.

I have always fancied myself as a bowler, but decided early on in my limited cricketing career that I had to be wicket-keeper because then I get to wear the big gloves and pads ... the ball is so bloody hard and it hurts if you're skilled or lucky enough to catch it. Geoffrey Darke, a retired local surgeon, had the same idea, so we kept wicket alternate years – in the end I had to give in to him as he was too old to run after the ball as a fielder (or that's what he said).

Huwie was a real disappointment to us. He had been given the partnership job because of his renowned athletic qualities on the rugby field. Brought on in his first year with us as our surprise talent, we discovered that while he had prodigious skills with a large, oval ball, he was completely useless with a small, round, red one. My batting philosophy is to hit the ball as hard as I can, and, consequently, I'm rarely at the wicket for long. My crowning glory, if I can claim any, was to put the ball through Miss Northover's greenhouse – her house bordered the middle school sports ground. The shattering glass had a strangely evocative effect: the immediate reaction of us all was to stand stock still – as in days of old when it had been parent's or school's windows – and wait for the repercussions. Fortunately for us, Miss Northover was a radio-grapher in the Minehead Hospital X-ray department and did not deal with us too harshly.

Now the new rules of drug-company sponsorship have put a stop to the fund-raising element of the game, but we continue the tradition and now play just for the fun (and/or the humiliation) of it all. Events like this make up a life that is enjoyably balanced, in a relatively small community. In Minehead I have found that there is little kudos just in being a doctor, a lawyer or an Indian chief. If you are not prepared to become part of the community then the community will not come to meet you. It is widely accepted that you will remain an 'incomer' until you have been here at least three generations, but you will be willingly adopted if airs and graces are left where they are 'better' appreciated. As a result of this attitude we share in a surprisingly close community for the end of the twentieth century and I think that my family and I have been fortunate to live a life that in some respects is more community-based than that we may have encountered had we decided to settle in a larger practice area.

Of course living in a small rural community has its disadvantages. Everyone knows everyone's business. You can be at a party on Saturday night and hear a report of your conversation and conduct on Monday morning from the aunt of the person you were talking to who turns out to be the sister of your receptionist who is the second cousin of the person you were talking about. In fact, in my first week

I was not alone in putting up such a poor show.

in Minehead I was out walking with the family when we were approached by two elderly women whom I had never set eyes on in my life before.

'Are you the new doctor?' they enquired.

'Yes.'

At that I was grabbed and firmly kissed on the cheek by both women who turned out to be either my second cousins or my first cousins once removed (I never understood the difference). Apparently my Great Uncle Fred, who had lived in Bampton Street in Minehead, had fathered five children and there were any number of my relatives living around and about. It is always sensible to bear in mind the nature of this close community when entering into any conversation or activity. The frantic disco-dancing on tables that seemed so amusing on Saturday night does not always seem so amusing on Monday morning when retold by the third person you meet, particularly when it is your cooler-than-cool 15-year-old daughter on her return from school or, in a certain teacher's experience, every parent and pupil on their way into school.

There are many advantages to living in a small community, but I suppose it depends on which side of the fence you are on – my poor daughter was certain she was on the wrong side when she was growing up and taking her first steps towards independence. When she went to the cinema with her first boyfriend, unknown to her, her mother or me, her every move was watched. The following day my wife Annie went shopping and was given an unasked-for report: 'They held hands but nothing else, and he acted very properly.' Someone, somewhere, is bound to know someone, somewhere, who knows you.

Sadly, things are changing, and at a remarkably fast pace, but there is still the sense of a true neighbourhood in Minehead. Neighbours do still watch out for their neighbours, but unlocked front doors are becoming a thing of the past (but only the recent past). Annie was the co-ordinator of the Victim Support Scheme ten years ago and had no victims to support for the whole of the year. Professionally, as far as she was concerned, it was a great disappointment. Having been on the courses she was ready and more than willing to support all and sundry, but day after day the police had no reports of personal crime. Now, 10 years later, it is a different picture. As a doctor I have seen the increase in drug use, which is now commonplace among children you would not have expected to be involved with drug culture. As the size of the town increases the internal checks are weakened. You may now get away with dancing on tables without the whole town knowing … but I don't think I'll risk it.

On the face of it, life still ticks on as it has since I first arrived, but the annual lifeboat cricket match seems to epitomize a pace of life that is slowly but surely disappearing, and whether the next generation will experience it, I don't know. My children are scattered round the world: one is in London, one in Australia and one in America. My youngest is still at home and enjoying the quad race track, but I anticipate that he will leave in due course. Whether any of them will return has yet to be seen. A town nearly 30 miles from a motorway has limited appeal to a youngster itching to discover the world. It is a wonderful place to grow up, as there is a freedom that comes with an accessible countryside. The woods around our farm are littered with camp sites and tree houses set up by our children and their friends from the age of five upwards. The early ones were simple camps built in the bushes, developing to a hair-raising den built at the top of a 40-foot tree at the end of the farm track. That one was built by Ben and his friend James Lock when they were about 12, and I insisted on checking it before they invited their friends to have picnics in it. It was a case of making sure that it was basically safe and then closing our eyes when they were in it.

The most exciting aspect of the tree-house was the rope swing that allowed them to swing from the tree out over the drive, and thereby so alarm visitors to the farm that they were in grave danger of driving over the cliff. Annie gave up all responsibility for the children at this time. However, I stood firmly behind the boys in their support of the den – in truth, I wished it had been mine. The idea of sitting out of sight some 40 feet above the ground and then watching the adults' reactions when they looked up through the branches reached a deep part of my childhood soul and I decided the risks were worth running. Strangely enough, I'm not at all sure that I will let my grandchildren reinstate the tree house – perhaps I'm getting old. In any event, I know that I would not now want to climb the tree to check it out. An annual game of cricket is one thing, but scaling the limbs of an ancient maple tree is quite another. I wonder if the Duphalac Man would be interested in sponsoring me branch by branch?

10
Dr Bodgett's
Match-winning Embrocation

As a doctor I know the importance of regular exercise, just as I know the importance of a healthy diet. Knowing is not the same as living, and as I hated playing compulsory sports at school I was surprised to find, when I got to medical school, that people played rugby football voluntarily and for pleasure. It was Chris Peach, now a London GP but then one of my flatmates, who invited me to play and started me off on my far from illustrious rugby career.

We played for the Charing Cross Hospital Medical School Third Fifteen, better known as The VOMITS (Veterans, Old Men, Idiots and Twits). We were a terrible side that turned out every Saturday to be soundly beaten by the opposition. Our crowning glory was to lose 98 points to three against Esher Twelfths, the three points being scored by myself crawling with the ball through the base of the scrum. As it was the only time I ever had any score credited to my name, I had no intention of admitting the illegality of the move to a partially sighted referee.

I did not play again until we came to live in Minehead and was invited to play for the Minehead Barbarians Third Team. Graham Lawrence, mainstay of the Minehead Barbarians and now, I'm proud to say, a close friend, took a look at my build and mistakenly took me for a front-row forward. Because of my appalling ball-handling skills, and my expert ability to fall over in the mud when changing direction, not to mention my general state of unfitness, my main contribution to the Third Fifteen was that of team doctor.

For some reason, my presence gave the team a sense of confidence. This meant that instead of being dropped as soon as my lack of skills became apparent, I was allowed to pretend to play as a prop forward and, more importantly, was in charge of the bucket and sponge. In the pre-AIDS days, when blood was regarded as a trophy rather than a potential source of danger, the bucket of bloodstained water, with a tatty piece of mud-caked sponge, was the mainstay of the therapeutic armament and was the source of all cures for all injuries sustained on the field of play. The slogan 'Give blood – play rugby' was a popular car sticker.

It didn't take me long to realize that being the medic on the pitch could give our team some useful advantages. A cut eyebrow in one of our players might need a quick wipe with the sponge, an encouraging pat on the shoulder and on with the game. If an opposition player sustained the same injury I would take a long time examining the wound and then pronounce in my gravest of tones that the injury was serious and needed immediate transfer to the casualty department for professional attention. Any dissent from quasi-medics of the opposition could easily be quashed by mumbling something like, '... will never be able to see again ...', or for leg injuries, '... never be able to walk again ...', and the victim would be rushed off to hospital by a willing spectator. Replacement players were unheard of – it was hard enough to get a team of 15 together – so getting one or two of the opposition into the casualty department waiting room gave us a half-decent chance of victory. Using my orthopaedic skills to reduce dislocated fingers, and on one occasion the dislocated shoulder of an opposition player, usually impressed the rest of the players, but these activities on the field were not my only responsibility.

My pre-match duty was to prepare a supply of a special concoction invented with the help of local pharmacist Roy Hawkins, who was one of the original founders of the Barbarians. His chemist shop was full of old pointy bottles with glass stoppers, which contained interestingly coloured liquids. We searched the dusty shelves of his back room, finding pots of *unguentum capisci* and other things that he hadn't seen for years and didn't know he possessed. This and other secret ingredients were mixed together to make Dr Bodgett's Special Match-winning Embrocation, a foul, black-coloured, greasy substance, which rendered the air of the changing room unbreathable. It brought the team out in huge red weals, but it was a mark of manhood to plaster it all over oneself in generous handfuls. One day we front-row forwards had the bright idea of putting a dollop of Dr Bodgett's on the top of our heads so that when we went down in the first scrum the opposition would get it in their eyes, rendering them blind, and giving us an excellent playing advantage. It worked well for the first five seconds, after which the foul mixture spread throughout the whole of the two packs leaving us all, eyes streaming, staggering around the field and trying to feel our way to the bucket and sponge.

I once had an alarming case of snow blindness to treat. Returning from a long weekend tour of north Cornwall we stopped at North Tawton to play a game. High on the moors, it had snowed all morning and we had to dig the snow off the line markings to reveal the whereabouts of the pitch. In an interesting manoeuvre our winger, Andre Baker, missed a tackle and slid elegantly headfirst into a snowdrift, disappearing up to his chest. As he crawled out backwards, his face covered in ice, he started shouting in panic, 'I can't see ... I'm blind, I'm blind ...' As I wheezed my way through the biting air to cross the pitch and go to his aid, I was trying to work out what sort of dreadful injury he might have sustained from a faceful of snow, but could think of none.

Andre certainly could not see. His understandable panic resulted in an unusual cross-team concern and, when I knelt down by my fellow Barbarian, we were surrounded by 28 worried players, as well as the referee, the spectator and his dog. Thankfully, I quickly saw that cold and panic had resulted in Andre's eyes being tightly shut in a reactive spasm. The bucket and sponge were frozen solid and it struck me that this was the perfect situation for my first 'putting-on of hands'. I had been keeping my hands warm throughout the game by keeping them firmly in my pockets. This had caused no detriment to the quality of my play as I had managed to stay well away from the ball for most of the match, so I now had the perfect healing instruments at the ends of my wrists. I put my warm hands against his eyes and suggested that he try opening them. On doing so he found his sight miraculously rediscovered – as was the team's faith in my medical abilities.

My medical expertise was not always so gratefully received. During one particularly hard game Danny Williams, our one-eyed lock forward, had his ear badly ripped.

'Do you want the bucket, Danny?' I offered.

'No. What ... I want,' said Danny, 'is revenge.'

It was Danny who prompted the end to my playing days. At an Easter festival of veteran over-35's rugby, when most sensible people were lazing in the spring sunshine, I followed him into a ruck. As he stamped his foot down I managed to get my own foot in the way. At the same time, as he wrestled the ball from an opposing player, he smacked the point of his elbow sharply on to the end of my nose. With a broken toe and a faceful of blood I limped to the side of the field knowing that I was too old and too delicate to be doing this sort of thing. As soon as I got home I put my boots into the Rayburn. A fine gesture at the time, but it meant the following week I had to borrow, ashamedly, a pair of boots from my son Ben.

For many years the Minehead Barbarians have been developing mini-rugby for children from the age of six upwards. When I started taking my two older boys, Ben and Oliver, we were able to get a few teams of mixed ages together for matches with other clubs. The minis have now grown to around 120 players turning out every Sunday for training. As well as local, county and now national festivals we have had an international connection for a number of years. In the early 1980s the Barbarians developed a close relationship with Plouzane Club de Rugby in Brittany, for both mini and adult rugby, with teams visiting each other on a regular basis. Parents and mini-players stay in club members' homes and both children and adults have formed lasting friendships. In 1989, for the 200th anniversary celebrations of the French Revolution, we were invited to a mini tournament. Both Ben and Oliver were playing and I went as a parent and, of course, as team doctor.

My main responsibility was to administer the seasickness pills for the ferry crossing. As I have always been a terrible sailor it was more a 'physician heal thyself' scenario – I have been known to feel quite queasy just watching the ferry from the quayside. The only time I have ever been present when there has been an announcement of the old cliché, 'Is there a doctor on board?' was when I was travelling back from Germany with the family on a ferry crossing from Zeebrugge. We were in a force 8 gale, ship rolling all over the place, crockery smashing everywhere. I was so drowsy with anti-emetics that I could not answer the call. When I was eventually roused to take notice I found that a lorry driver had split his head on a table edge as one of the nauseous swells had tipped the boat half on to its side. In the event, when I managed to shake myself sufficiently alert to attempt to tend to the poor chap, I was pushed out of the way by a nurse who was taking it much more seriously. When she said,

'Move aside, I'm a nurse,' I did, and returned to my sick bed in every sense of the phrase.

The adults on the mini-rugby trips take their responsibilities seriously and the most serious of those responsibilities is providing sufficient food to satisfy the constantly starving boys and their fathers. Graham Lawrence was appointed Officer in Charge of the catering arrangements on one of the trips and neatly side-stepped mass catering by telling everyone to take their own packed lunch, and in his own case getting his wife, Rose, to make his sandwiches. She made plenty of them and filled a catering-size margarine tub which she left in the fridge. On leaving the house Graham grabbed the tub at the last moment and rushed down to catch the coach. When we finally arrived on board the ferry we spread ourselves on the deck in the most glorious sunshine and settled down to enjoy our picnics. Graham, beers at hand and getting up his salivation, stated that his wife made the best sandwiches and pondered aloud, 'I wonder what we're having this time?' With much showmanship he opened the lid of his margarine tub – and quickly shut it – opened it again slowly and looked at us in total disbelief. In the rush to leave the house he had grabbed a tub full of margarine. To add insult to injury the margarine had gone soft in the heat, and in his disappointment he managed to tip the container and pour the warm grease all over his trousers. The memories of this often recounted disaster reduce grown men and their boys to tears, and to this day Graham can never be offered a sandwich without someone recalling the magic moment.

As all those involved with sports clubs know, there is a considerable amount of time and effort that goes into fund-raising, and the major fund-raising event at the rugby club in recent years has been the summer ball, which we modelled on the rather glorious balls we had attended while serving with the RAF. The rugby club balls started in a relatively small way, but over the years developed into big events with marquees, bands, string quartets, jugglers and fire-eaters, bouncy castles and firework displays.

The first year, four of us organized the ball. Sue Waterman, a local vet, was in charge of catering. My wife set about transforming the clubhouse into a suitably flower-bedecked venue and Jim Waterman and I sorted out the entertainment and marquees. All went well until the day before the ball when the fire officer called to inspect the club and condemned the decorations as being a fire hazard. True in retrospect, but it meant we had to work all night to redecorate the whole of the main hall. More dramatically, on the afternoon of the ball, Sue was dressing a shark, which was to be the centrepiece of the banquet, when she managed to run her finger along one of its teeth, resulting in a deep and extremely painful cut requiring a number of stitches. Somehow or other that piece of news managed to make the national newspapers, along with the headline 'Dead shark bites vet!'

Once the finger had been stitched and the hall redecorated, the ball went ahead and was a great success, becoming an annual event. That first year taught us a lot about organizing large events, not least that we should have recruited washers-up for the following day. When the guests were all gone, we had to get the cutlery and china sorted out to be returned, so the four of us, with some valiant friends, rolled up our sleeves and worked on through the next day. One of the best volunteers was a wonderful woman who was holidaying in a caravan at the far corner of the rugby ground. When she turned up at the clubhouse for her morning ablutions she saw us all still in our finery, up to our elbows in suds, and just waded in and washed up for the whole of the morning. She insisted on doing the greasiest of the washing up, refused any payment and provided sufficient cheerful enthusiasm to prevent us from sleeping where we stood. We eventually staggered home late that afternoon having been at the club for a straight 36 hours. One of the lasting images of that endless day was my father, mid-afternoon still dressed in his dinner suit, stolidly walking the length of the rugby field fetching glasses. The poor man was so exhausted that instead of taking a tray with him and gathering a number of glasses in one go, he was picking up one glass at a time and then walking back to the clubhouse, turning round and walking back up the pitch to collect another single glass.

Despite continuing to play after I had burned my boots, I was eventually persuaded by my ageing body that playing rugby was not really very wise. I only played in the special veteran matches, and without training and regular exercise I was at risk of dropping dead mid-game. A glorious way to go, no doubt, but I still have things I'd like to do. My rugby-playing sons have now moved on and so, sadly, I now have little active involvement with the club. However, it strikes me that as I settle into middle age I have at last discovered the best way to enjoy sport – in retrospect, and from the comfort of an armchair.

11

Afternoon Surgery

Our practice annual report has been produced this week. Each year it gets larger and this year is no exception. Like most documents of this type it has a page at the beginning that spells out our 'mission statement'. (Does anyone take those things seriously or do we all cringe when we read them?) If the mission statement doesn't induce an immediate state of boredom and stop you going any further, the report goes on to make interesting reading. One set of figures confirms what we have all suspected – that the number of consultations we have had has increased dramatically in the last 12 months. In common with all GP practices, the figures further show that women attend far more often than men. This is not because women are less healthy – far from it, as we also know that female life expectancy is greater than male – but they tend to have a different approach to their health. This is well borne out by the first patient I see in surgery this afternoon.

Nora is in her early eighties, though to look at her you would think she is at least a decade younger, and she has been on the waiting list for some months for a washout and steroid injection into her arthritic knee. She lives some distance from the local shops and has been having great difficulty getting back up the hill to her house: recently she has resorted to a taxi for the last half-mile home. On top of that she has been experiencing more symptoms from a vaginal prolapse that has been present for a couple of years. A prolapse is where the womb is no longer supported by the weakening pelvic floor muscles. The result is that the womb drops down, pressing on the bladder and causing a 'dragging' sensation. She has been offered surgery for it in the past, but turned it down because the symptoms were not really too troublesome but now, with the need to know the whereabouts of every available toilet in town, she has changed her mind. Her gynaecologist had tried to postpone matters by fitting a ring pessary, a plastic device inserted into the vagina to support the womb, but it fell out within 24 hours. Nora phoned me for advice and saw the gynaecologist again four days ago. I received a letter from her consultant only this morning telling me that Nora had accepted the offer of surgical repair and had been put on the 'soon' waiting list. The purpose of Nora's consultation is to confirm that she is doing the right thing, to be clear that I know what is happening and generally to get everything straight and organized in her mind. We have a chat about it all and I confirm that I agree with the plan.

At the end of the consultation she pulls out a sheet of paper from her handbag.

'Can you please sign this for Bill?'

Bill is her husband. He has had a bladder tumour for the last two years and has to go into hospital every three to six months for a check-up. The tumour is in the form of small warty growths on the lining of the bladder, and if any new growth is found with the operative telescope it can be burnt away with a hot wire. Bill would much rather disregard his tumour and finds it a real nuisance to have to go to hospital so often. Part of ignoring it is to avoid coming to the surgery to have the pre-anaesthetic form filled in – he would much rather have Nora deal with it than come to the surgery himself.

As our annual report reflects, the difference in approach to treatment shown by Bill and Nora is not at all unusual. Of course, there are exceptions, but often we find that our women patients want to know all the whys and wherefores and will come to the surgery with informed questions, seeking to understand their illness and treatment. Many male patients will only come after prompting from their wives or families and then will reluctantly give their symptoms and leave as soon as possible. Often I think there is a feeling that if the symptoms are ignored they may go away. Other times, it is a fear that as the symptoms haven't gone away it may be something serious and it's easier to try to forget it all than face an unwelcome diagnosis. As, more often than not, patients present themselves with eminently treatable complaints, the male, ostrich-type attitude to ill health can lead to weeks or months of unnecessary worry. Anticipating this can prove beneficial to both doctor and patient. Taking a few moments at the end of a consultation to give information – answering the questions that should have been asked, suggesting a relative might like to come with them next time – can all mean that treatment goes more smoothly and might encourage an early consultation should any problems occur in the future. Delay can sometimes mean that a minor matter becomes far more serious as it is left untreated. More of my time and resources are needed and the poor patient suffers unnecessary stress and extended medication and treatment. I don't want all our male patients to become hypochondriacs, but they could get much more from their consultations if they adopted Nora's intelligent, straightforward approach.

My next patient, Julie, has come with her brother and his girlfriend, neither of whom are on our list, for advice about their mother, Susan, who is also not registered with us. They are in a terrible dilemma over what to do with her. The story that they give is that their mother has simply stopped looking after herself. She doesn't eat unless food is put in front of her and she hasn't washed or bathed for months. She has been under the care of the psychiatric services and has spent time in hospital. Three months ago she was discharged home to be looked after by her own elderly mother and her son. None of them can cope any longer with the strain of her bizarre behaviour and they are at the end of their tether. Susan falls between the two stones of psychiatric and Social Services care. From the psychiatric point of view she is not an immediate danger to herself and therefore does not come within the scope of the Mental Health Act for treatment against her will. She will not take any medication and will not voluntarily come in to hospital again. From the Social Services point of view she refuses all offers and attempts to help her. In truth, she is only able to continue as she is with the regular assistance of her family. On one hand, they cannot bear to stop looking after her and, on the other, they know that they are allowing the situation to continue by doing so.

I spent some time explaining why we cannot force treatment on Susan. Under the Mental Health Act, people can be detained against their will if they are unwell enough to be detained in hospital for assessment or treatment. The difficulty in this case is that there is a further statutory requirement: that, unless detained, the patient will be a risk to themselves or to others. Left on her own, Susan would probably be at risk of harm from neglect. However, her caring family clean up after her, prepare food to tempt her to eat and make valiant attempts to assist her with her personal hygiene. They would continue to do so, but the stresses and strains of looking after their mother are considerable. In these circumstances, it is not the actual physical caring that is the real problem – it is watching someone you love, who is clearly unwell and could be helped, continue to decline.

If the condition cannot be treated then they could come to accept the situation and decide how best to cope, but they know that with the right medication their mother could return to live a happier and more fulfilling life. As long as she is well enough to be judged to have the capacity to make her own decisions, then her refusal to accept any help that Social Services may be able to offer will override the family's request for help. How can a loving family stop caring for their mother? But unless they stop caring, how else can they get their mother the help she obviously needs? Susan is not my patient, but is registered with another practice in the town, so I cannot seek to persuade her to accept treatment. I advise her family to speak to their mother's doctor, who may be able to persuade her to accept help. As far as the family is concerned, I can only listen and advise, and seek to defuse the high level of stress and distress they are all feeling.

David is 38 years old and is complaining of persistent indigestion-type pains in his upper abdomen. He tells me that he gets relief from taking an antacid medicine but the relief is only temporary. He has had it on and off for several years but it has only recently become severe and persistent enough to come to the surgery for help.

We regularly receive information and analysis about the drug prescriptions that we write and, although we have always been well below the national average for the amount of drugs we prescribe, our scripts for gastro-intestinal medications seem to increase all the time. There are now some extremely effective and safe drugs available for hyperacidity and stomach-ulcer symptoms and it is becoming a rarity to have a patient with acute and copious bleeding from the stomach. Twenty years ago the surgical wards were full of patients having partial gastrectomies and other operations to remove life-threatening stomach ulcers and I remember one particular incident in the casualty department in Canterbury when two patients on neighbouring trolleys in the crash room were both vomiting pints of blood from their haemorrhaging ulcers. I was hand-pumping blood transfusions into both at the same time and I remember the difficulty I had winding the handles, one in each hand, in the right direction. It was like trying to play the child's game of rubbing your tummy and

Huwie walks about half a mile each week collecting his patients from the waiting room.

patting the top of your head without getting confused – though with rather more dire consequences if I got it wrong. (Modern hospital house officers have it easy with these new-fangled electric pumps!)

David won't have that sort of trouble. He gives quite a long history of indigestion and it is possible that he is harbouring a particular bacterial stomach infection. The bug, called helicobacter pylori, is known to be associated with ulcers and chronic gastritis and if it is eradicated with a high-dose mixture of antibiotics the stomach can be completely cured. Until recently it has been difficult to decide who has the infection and who hasn't and diagnosis has been dependent on a biopsy sample taken with a telescope tube into the stomach. Now, however, we are able to detect antibodies to helicobacter with a simple finger-prick blood test. We keep several testing kits in the nurses' room and if Jenny or Angela are free I can often have the diagnosis within 10 minutes. I explain all this to David but, unfortunately for him, we occasionally allow our nurses some time off and they have both gone home. I will start him on an H2-antagonist medication to get his symptoms under control and he will return for the finger-prick test in the next few days.

The next patient is a small girl with nothing more than an upper respiratory infection, but it is a joy to see her. Scarlet has just had her second birthday and I well remember the day that she was born in the cottage at Selworthy. Tracy had wanted to have her baby at home as soon as she knew she was pregnant and there were no obstetric reasons why she should not. Everything went according to plan and Tracy even kindly obliged by going into labour at 9 a.m. on a day when I had an afternoon off, which was very convenient. At the end of surgery I had called Anne, our midwife, to check how things were going.

'She's about five centimetres dilated,' she said, 'and making good progress.'

Plenty of time to do two visits and a quick trip home to feed the pigs. What I hadn't made provision for was the fact that my sow had also gone into labour at the same time. What a dilemma – stay and deliver a dozen piglets or go and help with a singleton? No choice, really. I patted Patience on the head and wished her good luck and crossed over the hill to Selworthy.

It is generally the doctor's job at a home birth, while everyone else is frenetically tearing up sheets and preparing vats of boiling water, to instil an air of quiet confidence by standing around jingling loose change in the pocket, staring out of the bedroom window and making pleasantries about the beauty of the shrub border. Tracy had different ideas and while Buzz, her husband, took a break to make tea for the assembled company, I took his place kneeling opposite her and allowing her to squeeze all the blood from my hand while she went through her final contractions. A privilege indeed. Tea made and expectant father returned, Scarlet was born shortly afterwards with no complications at all, blue turning to pink as she discovered her lungs and let us all know of her presence.

And, two years on, here she is in my surgery, reminding me of an unforgettable day. She is a little poorly, but I am able to reassure them that she has nothing serious. Patience, by the way, had 12 on that occasion.

Another addition to this year's annual report is an item written by Kate Stoner, who runs the complementary health centre. We appointed Kate as manager at the beginning of the project and she has worked hard to create a thriving enterprise. From humble beginnings two-and-a-half years ago we now have over 20 practitioners regularly using the 10 consulting rooms at the centre in a variety of disciplines.

The Western approach to medicine is largely based around diagnosis. We listen to a patient's history, make a physical examination and, in some cases, arrange investigations and tests. When we have formed a diagnosis we are then in a position, while taking other factors into account, to prescribe treatment. Complementary medicine tends to treat symptoms and the attachment of a diagnostic label is less important. This is a useful approach when one is treating problems of function, as opposed to a disease process such as infection. Take for example a patient with irritable bowel syndrome, who may be suffering intermittent symptoms of abdominal pains, excessive wind and bowel upset with diarrhoea or constipation. We may sometimes investigate the patient to exclude specific inflammatory diseases or infection but with IBS all the investigations will be normal. We are then left to treat the symptoms with antispasmodic medications and dietary advice. At that point, conventional medicine really has little to offer over some of the many complementary approaches. I often suggest to patients with IBS that they see the dietary therapist and I have never had a patient who has done so feel disappointed. The only reservation I have with complementary medicine is the risk of missing a diagnosis

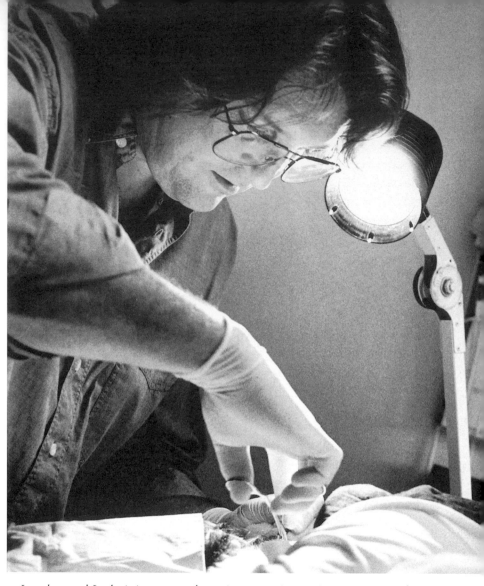

Jonathan and I take it in turns to do a minor operations session every two weeks.

that needs to be made early, but by having a 'conventional' and a complementary practice working alongside each other, none of us is working in isolation. We are all more likely to make an earlier referral – in both directions – and we like to think that our patients then get the best of both medical worlds.

The next patient in my surgery illustrates the benefit of the close working relationships we have formed with many of the complementary practitioners.

For many years Jean has suffered from migraine. Over time she has worked through all of the tablets, inhaler sprays and injections that we can offer and she really is not much better off than when she started seeing doctors. She gets some relief with our treatment when

she has an attack but preventative treatment and advice from us and a specialist on avoiding triggering factors is not particularly helpful. She still suffers regularly and each attack effectively takes 48 hours out of her life. It is very frustrating for us as well as her. Recently she read an article in a magazine on the possible benefit of acupuncture in migraine and, knowing that the complementary centre is associated with the surgery and that we may be generally supportive, wondered whether it might be suitable for her. Allan Johnstone has been providing acupuncture at Irnham Lodge since we started and he has had several sessions with Jean. She is really pleased with the results and tells me that although she still has attacks they are less frequent and nothing like as severe. It is a shame that I cannot, at present, refer her to an acupuncturist on the NHS. The saving in my prescription costs will be considerable if her improvement continues, as her injections cost £41 for a pack of two, and if she no longer needs them it would more than cover the cost of the consultations with Allan. Also, she is much better off with acupuncture, as the risk of side-effects is minuscule when compared to those of drug therapy. I look forward to the day when all my NHS patients can get this treatment and not just those who can afford it.

Homeopathy has a strange place in the NHS. It is not fundable routinely in general practice and yet it is available for patients in some centres, such as the Royal London Homeopathic Hospital in Queen Square in London. I have no doubt at all that patients benefit from homeopathy, though I can't possibly explain why. The scientific basis of homeopathy has never been understood or accepted by mainstream medicine and I am, after all, a mainstream doctor. Formal research into complementary medicine is pretty thin on the ground and we are hoping to do our bit to improve that. We are about to embark on a two-year research project, co-ordinated by the faculty of complementary medicine at Exeter University, which will look into the effect of homeopathy on childhood asthma. We have an ideal set-up here for research. For many years we have been collecting information about the diseases that we see, and the activities we get up to, and this means that at the push of several computer buttons we can identify all our young asthmatic patients and know what treatment they are on.

There is one area of complementary treatment that is not covered in our annual report – and a brief outline of the consultation I had with a patient some little while ago may explain why.

I knew there was something wrong with Barbara's eyes when I brought her in from the waiting room: she was all wide-eyed and couldn't blink properly. She launched immediately into the diet and bowel problem that was uppermost in her mind, and didn't let me get a word in edgeways. Throughout the consultation I couldn't help but stare at her eyes, which were giving her the appearance of a mad axe-woman. When we had finally settled the matter of the digestive disability she got up to leave.

'Are you having any trouble with your eyes, Barbara?'

'Oh that – yes. My eyelids have become all droopy. They keep falling down and I can't see properly.'

I looked at her eyes again and gently moved her lids with my thumb. Turning back to my desk I picked up my pen to write a note of her symptoms and having scribbled a few lines, tried to put my pen down – to find it was pretty well stuck to my fingers.

'Are your eyelids always this sticky?'

'Oh yes, that's the marmalade – if I put a bit on in the morning it dries up and holds my eyes open.'

I examined her again and found a sliver of orange peel, which confirmed her story. She told me that she hadn't wanted to trouble me with something so silly, and, anyway, I wouldn't be able to do anything about it. I did a couple of eye-movement tests to exclude any serious cause for her lid lag, such as a nerve dysfunction. The problem was that her 85-year-old skin had simply become too loose. I explained that a minor anaesthetic procedure would easily remove the redundant skin and she was pleased to accept the offer. I was in the ophthalmic clinic two days later so I sneaked her in as an extra patient and put her on the waiting list. The operation a couple of months later restored her eyelids to their former state and she was delighted. I have to say I thought this was a one-off, but only last month another patient came to see me. She had also developed droopy eyelids and had discovered the healing properties of marmalade!

I set about repeating the consultation with a sense of *déjà vu*, but nothing I could say would convince her to subject herself, even briefly, to the surgeon's knife. In the end the best advice I could give was something I remembered Barbara telling me – that Chivers has much better tacky qualities than Golden Shred.

I have considerable sympathy with anyone who is nervous about undergoing invasive treatment. I have to admit to being reluctant to attend my very pleasant and competent dentist's surgery unless I have reached a level of pain that would have me desperate enough to consent to having my head removed. Over the years I have encountered a number of imaginative and inventive self-remedies from similarly reluctant patients, and remember one particular chap who should have had his hernial trussing arrangements entered for a Design Centre Award.

Perhaps our next report should include a section on self-sufficiency – it could lead to a news sheet in which patients swap their own remedies and would certainly make for more amusing reading than anyone's mission statement.

12

Trial by Lunch

On 16 May 1997, our advertisement for a new assistant appeared in the *British Medical Journal*. We'd spent ages attempting to find the appropriate wording, but setting the right tone was the hardest part. Do you present the straightforward facts in the hope that you'll attract the serious-minded, conscientious young doctor who'll know the set-up from the start, or do you make it eye-catching and witty in order to lure those with a sense of fun and adventure? After much deliberation, we decided on the straightforward approach, and this is how the advertisement appeared:

PARTNERSHIP OFFERED: *Innovative West Somerset coastal practice requires a replacement for a half-time assistant to join our friendly five-doctor team. With the half-time senior partner retiring within the year, this post is anticipated to progress to partnership after approximately six months. We live and work in an extremely pleasant environment with plenty of country pursuits and water sports on our doorstep.*

Our senior partner, Tim Ross, has been with the practice for 29 years. Although Tim has reduced his hours by job-sharing with Huw's wife, Liz, the out-of-hours work is beginning to take its toll. During one of our weekly meetings last month, Tim suddenly revealed that he had something to announce. For a moment I thought he was going to say that he wanted to retire, but fortunately what he was suggesting was that he take the assistant GP's job in favour of his half-time partnership. This would mean he could continue taking surgery without the burden of extra hours and disruptive night shifts. I liked this idea and, with Tim setting the precedent, I shall look forward to doing the same as I approach retirement age. I call it 'hobby-doctoring' as Tim will now be able to pursue all his other interests – sailing, gardening and bee-keeping – with renewed enthusiasm. We decided that we should appoint a new assistant now with the idea that they will take over the partnership at the end of the year.

The number of doctors willing to enter general practice has diminished over the last ten years.

Liz Thomas is our only female doctor at present and as her children are still young, she works part-time. We were all in agreement that it would be an advantage to the practice to have a second woman doctor to replace Tim. Legally, you're not allowed to discriminate in the advertisement, but some practices get around it by including the phrase 'a personal interest in gynaecology and obstetrics preferred' (as recently seen in an advert for a partner in Pontefract), and realistically, like it or not, an interest in these specialities is an advantage. Many women prefer to discuss their personal problems with someone of the same sex. A normal day's surgery for Liz comprises 60 per cent women, so it's often a relief to her when a male patient walks through the door with something other than a gynaecological problem.

When I first came to Minehead 16 years ago, the practice was expanding in order to take on the work at the cottage hospital. Minehead Hospital had previously been staffed by surgical house officers, but in 1981 the responsibility was handed over to local GPs. As well as a small casualty department, the hospital has 40 beds – primarily for elderly care – and a variety of clinics in the out-patient department, staffed by visiting consultants. My application for the job was one of about 50 or 60 – mostly young doctors keen to enter general practice. The great joy of being a GP was the flexibility of the job – you could schedule your own surgeries, fit in home visits and have time to pursue other medical interests. When Tim Ross first became a general practitioner in the late 1960s, his working pattern was very different from the one we have now. With about 4000 patients between the three partners, a day's work was quite a leisurely affair for him. Surgery would start at 9.30 a.m., he'd nip home for a mid-morning coffee with his wife Moira, and fit in a few home visits before an unhurried lunch and a short afternoon surgery. Moira used to get very fed up because he was always around the house eating and drinking. Now, our working week is around 70 to 80 hours, which is a lot to tolerate in a 35-year working life. Consequently, it's becoming more and more difficult to attract suitable applicants. We were recently discussing our own appointments and realized that a 'suitable applicant' was someone who, as well as having the necessary medical qualifications, would fit into the community on a social level. For example, when Huwie was interviewed in 1989, our local rugby club was desperately in need of an injection of talent. As an ex-flanker for Glamorgan Wanderers, there was no doubt that Huwie should be offered the post. As well as being an ex-army man, Jonathan Driscoll is also a keen sailor and has proved to be a useful crew member for Tim's 28-foot yacht. On that basis, I'm not sure why I was offered the post.

In the last 10 years the number of doctors willing to enter general practice has diminished significantly. Seventy-five willing candidates applied for the partnership in 1989, but only 10 applications trickled through the post two years ago when we last advertised. As a junior hospital doctor, long hours are tolerable, but as you become more senior the novelty soon wears off. The prospect of a lifetime of out-of-hours work is daunting, even for the most conscientious new doctor and, with a family to raise and a home to run, it requires a lot of negotiation with your partner to establish a workable lifestyle.

The results of our advertisement this time have provided a rather disappointing response. However, there are three or four applications which interest us and today it is Rianne and Stephanie who are coming to meet us at the practice. We have a tradition at Irnham Lodge that interviews are more of a trial-by-lunch affair than a stuffy conversation over the boardroom table. It's important that the candidate feels relaxed and discovers as much about us as we do about them. Consequently our schedule for the day ran as follows:

11.00 a.m. Rianne arrives for a chat with Paul Slade and Jonathan Driscoll in common room and tour of the surgery.

12.00 p.m. Stephanie has lunch with Jonathan Driscoll and his wife at home.

12.30 p.m. Huw Thomas and Tim Ross take Rianne and her husband to lunch at The Spoonful of Sugar.

Plenty of country pursuits and watersports on our doorstep.

2.00 p.m. Paul Slade takes Stephanie on a tour of Minehead and a look around the cottage hospital.

3.30 p.m. All doctors meet Stephanie for an informal interview.

Rianne is 30 and just completing her six-months vocation GP training at a neighbouring practice in Somerset. Having studied in Holland she came to this country two years ago to complete her training and she is now looking to settle here with her husband. As she knows Chris, our registrar, quite well, I'm sure she has already heard a lot about our set-up here. She is coming to look at the surgery today and to meet the partners, but she is not coming for a formal interview.

Stephanie is currently working as a GP registrar in Hampshire and would like to move west with her husband and three children. She came down with her family last weekend and stayed with Huw and Liz in order to get a feel for the area. Huw was very much impressed (which could well have been due to the fact that she listed sailing as one of her interests), but Stephanie has been offered another job which she is considering taking, hence our need to see her today.

At 11.00 a.m. I met up as planned with Rianne. (Actually, it was 11.15 as I'd had a rather complicated session with one of my elderly

patients who suffers badly with arthritis. When I asked to have a look at the foot which was causing her problems, she had terrible difficulty undoing her suspenders with her arthritic hands and so I found myself – with, incidentally, only occasional experience in this area – giving her a helping hand.) I liked Rianne instantly and we got chatting about our previous night's experience 'on call'. Actually, it turned out that I wasn't supposed to be on call at all, but at 3.00 a.m. I'd had a phone call from Chris Salway asking my advice about a patient with acute paranoia who he was dealing with. In my sleepy state I had asked him if he would like me to come and give him a hand, having assumed that I was covering him on night duty (we always have a doctor on standby when the registrar covers nights, in the eventuality that something like this may occur). I stayed with Chris until 7.00 a.m. and then suggested we nip down to the Blue Spot Café for a breakfast fry-up. It wasn't until this moment that I discovered it was actually Huwie who was supposed to be covering him, but Chris had been unable to get in touch with him and so had phoned me instead and was surprised when I offered my services.

While Huwie and Tim took Rianne to lunch, I nipped home to feed the pigs on last night's left-over pasta before meeting Stephanie for our tour of the town. I'm not sure I made the greatest impression as I led her out of the surgery towards the Land Rover. It has seen better days, I know, but I'd made the effort to dust down the front seats and remove any unsavoury farming debris. It's just a shame that when she came to open the passenger door, no amount of effort would prize it open and so in the end she had to enter on the driver's side and clamber over the gearstick. I had hoped to take her up to the farm but after a scenic tour of Minehead's attractions and a quick whiz around the hospital, there simply wasn't time. Never mind, we enjoyed each other's company and discussed children, grandchildren, where to buy a house, and skiing. I have never been skiing, but at least I could describe the joys of sliding down the hill from the farm on a plastic feed bag.

When we all gathered to meet Stephanie for a more formal interview, most of the conversation was geared to out-of-hours work and I think we confused her completely by attempting to explain the rota. At one point, Jon disappeared downstairs to get a copy of our monthly schedules but, with all credit to Penny, our head receptionist, for compiling them, you have to have worked here for at least a year before you can even begin to understand them.

Stephanie: 'So, when you're on call, how much time is actually spent on duty?'

Jon: 'Well, there's two types of weekend. You'll either have a working weekend when you're doing approximately half a weekend which will be a Saturday morning and afternoon, or a Sunday night … and then that same week you would also do two nights.'

Huw: 'And then the other nights you will be on standby.'

Tim: 'At the moment we're doing one in three and a half. So your commitment will be one week in seven.'

Stephanie: 'Right.'

Huw: 'It's a normal working week except that on the days you do nights you don't come in in the mornings and don't come in the morning after …'

Stephanie: 'And what about your second on-call?'

Tim: 'There might be three nights when you're on standby.'

Paul: 'The way we're doing it at the moment is that two of us are doing a weekend. One of those would be designated as first on, and they get the choice of doing nights or days. The other person who did the duty weekend with them is off …'

Despite our inability to make it crystal clear, Stephanie seemed keen, and although she has some strong opinions about various areas of our work, they are opinions that we all share.

We met up at the end of a hectic day, and all agreed that we would be happy to work with both Rianne and Stephanie. Both had a lot to offer and would make very good GPs. However, a decision had to be made and Stephanie had more experience, having completed her vocational training and now working as a GP registrar, so we decided we should offer her the post. She has definite ideas about her commitment both to her work and to her family and her experience in obstetrics and accident-and-emergency work is exactly what we are looking for. I can see her fitting in very well to our working family and I shall look forward to the introduction of some fresh blood when she takes up the post. I also feel comforted by the fact that, as Tim will be staying on as assistant, we will still have the benefits of his lifetime experience in general practice.

13

A Latin Term Too Far

As I was preparing to leave casualty late this afternoon I glanced through the window of the sister's office and noticed my wife's car pulling up outside the entrance and my son Oliver gingerly hauling himself from the passenger seat. It was a pleasant early summer's evening and, ever optimistic, my first thought was that they had come to collect me for an impromptu soirée. It was then I realized that Oliver was hobbling across the tarmac with shoe in hand and a pained expression on his face. As I opened the casualty door to greet him I saw the look of horror when he realized that I was the doctor on duty. Oliver had stubbed his toe rather badly while playing basketball with his friends and, thinking that it might be broken, had persuaded Anne to bring him in, in search of succour. The prospect of his own father being capable of administering to his needs was unthinkable. In fact, he was reluctant to let me even take a look and preferred the nurse on duty to make a valued opinion as to the extent and significance of his injury – which incidentally turned out to be no more than bad bruising.

I know that my children are not alone among the offspring of GPs in being able to recount any number of incidents of medical child-neglect. My eldest son's favourite is the weekend he spent suffering an undiagnosed broken arm. On Monday morning, when my considered advice to rub it better and to stop making such a fuss had not resulted in any improvement, to keep some level of domestic harmony I arranged for an X-ray. Smug is the term that best covers the collective family expression when Ben and I returned home, with his arm encased in plaster.

General practice is a way of life as much as a job. The hours are irregular and calls come at all times of the day and night. I realize that a GP is not alone in this and that there are many other occupations that encroach on what might be seen as family time. Just as anyone who marries a soldier should not be planning to put down roots or anyone who marries a publican expect to share quiet evenings at home, anyone who marries a GP has to get used to having an irregular routine, and they should certainly not expect to have any degree of caring medical treatment.

Left to their own devices (or diagnoses) medical families are obliged to rely on the magical properties of mother's kiss or, if they are very lucky, a smearing of three-year-old crusty antiseptic cream and a yellowing plaster found lurking at the back of a kitchen drawer. It must be this necessity to self-diagnose that leads other people to expect doctors' families to have an expertise in their parent/spouse's field of work. My wife has been shown rashes and asked to give a quick diagnosis (correctly confirmed as chicken-pox) and to give advice as to what to do for cold feet (her diagnosis that the patient was over-reacting was not confirmed, the case proving to be one of advanced gangrene).

In reality, I suspect doctors' families probably know less about medical matters than the rest of the population. Whereas the offspring of non-medical parents know to the nearest tenth of a degree what their temperature is when they have a cold, I cannot recall my children ever having seen a thermometer. A hand to the forehead gives a perfectly adequate reading of 'you're fine' or 'you're a bit hot'. The usual procedure for treating the family is first to ignore, if they persist to offer the good old standby 'there's a lot of it going around' and finally to rummage in the misnamed medicine tin and offer something vaguely related to the ailment. The tin is misnamed in that it is crammed to bursting, but contains very little that could be described as medical – ten summers' worth of suntan lotion, packets of cat wormers, several bottles of half-used nit lotion and a variety of dog-flea shampoos. Fortunately, my family is remarkably healthy and I found that when they were younger I could get by with an all-purpose antiseptic cream and an antiseptic spray of some kind. Smear or spray with sufficient confidence and, until the children are old enough to start to question the omniscience of their parents, faith in the sprayer seems to be enough.

As every parent of teenage children knows, there comes a point where the blind faith your children had in you turns almost overnight to a committed conviction that you know nothing and that nothing you say can be relied upon. It may be something to do with the discovery that the 'pork' they had been happily eating for years had in fact been eligible for a part in *Watership Down* or the fact that the spray I had been convincingly spraying on stings was in fact a spray for burns. In any event, I found I had to change tactics.

I have always tried to explain medical matters in simple English, avoiding Latin terms wherever possible. However, the time came when telling one of my children he had a strained finger that would get better in a couple of days proved unacceptable. He didn't believe I knew anything about damaged hands and his brothers and sister declared their complete disbelief in my medical prowess. Taking his hand and looking at it for some time I then declared that he had 'traumatic tendonitis' (a strained finger that would get better in a couple of days). They were impressed, and for a few weeks I resumed my role of all-knowing medical man. Unfortunately, I got carried away with my success, and when my daughter showed me her sore throat I gravely announced she had a 'follicular pharyngitis'. It was a Latin term too far. As one voice, the family declared I was making it up. Over the next few days I was constantly shown various alleged strains and muscular injuries. It turned out that they were comparing my Latin diagnoses so they could catch me out making up medical gobbledegook. The trouble is that since the rabbit débâcle I'm on shaky ground when trying to convince them of my honesty credentials. Not wishing to bang my head (or my paternal ego) against a brick wall, I decided that the best thing to do was to refer all future ailments to the surgery and the family now make appointments and go and consult a 'proper doctor'. Fortunately, I have seldom needed to look beyond the medical tin's all-purpose cream and/or spray for my few minor ailments. It may be just as well, as my wife would have everyone believe that I am a dreadful patient.

For some reason it is a cause of great amusement that I faint at the sight of my own blood. I can happily cope with buckets of other people's blood, but show me a drip of my own and my fight-and-flight instincts become fright-and-drop. The first time this weakness came to light was at medical school when, as pre-clinical students, we had to take blood from each other. While colleagues spent their time usefully studying blood cells down microscopes I was being encouraged to get up off the floor by the lecturer, assisted by way of

a traditional slap to the face and threats of a bucket of cold water (more of the sympathetic approach later). The next time I dropped was one Christmas. I was cutting up the turkey for a Boxing Day stew when I sliced through my thumb. It didn't bleed at first, but by the time I got upstairs to the bathroom to rummage for the all-purpose cream the blood had started to flow. When I came round I admit that, initially, my wife did show some concern, but on finding all I had done was nick my thumb interest waned and I didn't even get a magic kiss better. A tatty plaster applied, I was left lying on the bed, pale as a ghost, to listen to my wife endlessly repeating the amusing tale to the extended family who were gathered for the Christmas celebrations.

To this day I harbour a grudge against my spouse about the following incident and I have never been able to convince her that her behaviour and attitude left me suitable for counselling for post-traumatic stress disorder. We had recently moved to a house that needed a lot of internal alterations. I was heaving a wheelbarrow full of the rubble from the old fireplace out of the front door, and had the misfortune to catch the back of my hand against the letter box. The blood flowed like it had never flowed before and I dropped in a way I had never dropped before. I was in no fit state to decide what should be done, but my wife, having heard the distressed whimper that preceded my collapse, took a quick look at my hand and decided that the medicine tin was not going to meet the challenge. Propped against the front door and taking great care not to look at my hand again, it was clear to me I needed to get to casualty as a matter of some urgency. As we lived less than a mile from the hospital I anticipated being there within the next five minutes. My wife piled the children into the car where they started a trawl of the 'dad fainting' stories and to a chorus of laughter we started off on a tour of West Somerset.

My beloved's version is that she was taking the back roads so as to avoid any traffic hold-ups. As at that time of year the traffic was very light and in any event there was never much traffic (the nearest traffic lights were 25 miles away) – traffic hold-ups were not renowned in our locality. I am assured we arrived at casualty within 20 minutes but, as I recall the scenic tour, an hour seems more likely. When we eventually arrived at the hospital I felt too weak to get out of the car and the family went to summon help. The response was impressive, with every member of staff on duty in casualty coming out to the car. Had the circumstances been different I might have been gratified to have been the cause of so much amusement, but given my weakened condition I felt the merriment to be somewhat misplaced. These were experienced professional medical staff, my colleagues, trained to empathize with their patients and to offer support and comfort, but where were they in my hour of need? I gathered that my face was a rather interesting shade of green, but did not really appreciate listening to the finer points of the debate, as my former friends tried to find just the right shade to describe my pallor ... enough said, I was eventually stitched up – both my hand and my reputation.

Interestingly, my eldest son has inherited this ability to drop at the first sight of his own blood. We discovered this one evening when he was cutting up an apple. From an adjoining room we heard a whimper, the tap being run and then nothing. After a few minutes his mother put two and two together and he was found lying on the kitchen floor.

That's my boy!

14

Hestercombe House Revisited

It was my grandfather's birthday last month and, as no doubt my mother would like me to recall, he would have been 107 had he not died. He came into my mind because I had recently been on a two day course at Hestercombe House and it was my grandfather who first took me there in the early 1960s. The house, just north of Taunton, was built around 1750. In the 1950s it was purchased by Somerset County Council and a little later was taken over as the headquarters of the Somerset fire brigade. The first time I visited Hestercombe I must have been about 10 years old. My grandfather, who was an independent county councillor, was attending a meeting of the fire committee and took my cousin Richard and me along with him. Richard and I had a great day, clambering over the fire engines, ringing the silver fire bells. We imagined that we were single-handedly extinguishing the Great Fire of Taunton and we were the heroes of the day.

My second visit to Hestercombe was not anything like as exciting as my first (the only reminder of the fire brigade was the fire drill, which was held before the course started), but it was nice to have a break from the usual routine, and the course on the management of drug addiction proved interesting. Since the 1960s drug addiction has been regarded as an inner-city problem, but over the last few years it has crept into our rural populations and is now a regular part of our daily practice. In the West Country, as a result of cannabis being in short supply and heroin becoming easily and cheaply available, we have recently seen an upsurge in heroin addiction.

Obviously, our eventual goal when treating addicts is to free them of their dependency but, with heroin dependency in particular, this can take a long time. With the best will of the doctors, drug counsellors and the patients themselves, our efforts often fail and the patient's addiction keeps its miserable hold. In those circumstances our realistic goal is to reduce the harm caused as a result of the drug addiction – harm to the patient, their family, and society at large.

The main problem GPs have in treating drug addicts is the amount of time that needs to be invested in a single patient. For those seriously intent upon breaking their dependency, the fortnightly visit to their GP is their lifeline. A regular supply of prescribed methadone means they do not have to worry about where their next fix is coming from, but for some this is not enough, and they sell their prescription to buy illegal drugs and/or top their methadone up with booze. At the fortnightly visits a urine test is undertaken: a positive urine test leads to the addict's suitability for the programme being reassessed, and if, after that assessment, it is decided that the commitment necessary is not present then they will be removed from the programme. It is depressing to have to tell someone that they have been excluded, but without the will to break the dependency we stand no chance of success.

Take, for example, a current patient of mine, Paul, whom I have known for 15 years. We have tried several times to get him off drugs by admitting him to hospital for detoxification, or by gradually reducing his methadone over long periods of time. Sadly, it always gets to a certain point and something goes wrong. I spend four or five hours' consultation time each year just dealing with his drug addiction, which is far more time than I give to my regular patients. I want to be Paul's doctor as well as his drug counsellor and prescriber, but writing the prescriptions, taking regular urine tests and discussing his plans for the future take up all the time I can give him, so his other medical problems – his asthma, his eczema – tend to get put on the back burner. Ideally, Minehead would have its own drug centre where users could be assessed, counselled, treated and receive their prescriptions. I could then revert to being Paul's GP again. The dilemma we are facing at the moment is that we simply do not have the time to take on any new drug users.

We are fortunate in that the practice is assisted by Bridget Broom, who is a community psychiatric nurse working specifically with drug users in this part of Somerset. When I was a medical student there was no training in drug management and I was terribly naïve. Bridget helps us to understand the day-to-day struggles faced by those we are treating, and her wealth of experience of working with addicts is invaluable to us. Bridget's experience and knowledge cannot be learned on courses or read in books. She knows when to be hard on her patients and when they need a sympathetic word. Most importantly, her patients know that there is no messing with Bridget. Play it straight and she is with you, but if the commitment is not there, then the programme will not be able to offer regular support. It is often hard for those who want treatment but cannot break the cycle of drug abuse. In those cases Bridget appears to be the enemy at times, and they feel they cannot get past her to get on a proper programme of treatment. However, experience shows that much time and money will be wasted if a real commitment to becoming drug- or alcohol-free is lacking.

Discussing individual patients with Bridget enables us to gain an insight into what is happening outside the surgery. On a recent visit, she described the experience of one of our patients who is attempting to give up heroin. At 21, Darren has decided that it is time to reform his life and attempt to become drug-free. He has used drugs every day of his life from the age of 15 and lives at home with his parents who, until quite recently, were unaware of his drug habit. Their first reaction was to 'rescue him': if he built up debts in order to buy drugs, they would pay them off and if he didn't have money for food they would buy it for him. This proved a fruitless remedy, and recently Darren started on a course of treatment with the full support of his parents. Although Darren is a 21-year-old man, he is still their child and, while trying to be good parents, they feel totally helpless as they try to understand this alien world.

The first day of his treatment went without a hitch. By the second day, Darren had become more aware of the psychological importance of drug dependence and suffered a great deal of emotional turmoil. A village on the edge of Exmoor is not the best place to invite sympathy for drug addiction. Rumour and gossip are rife and Darren felt isolated and misunderstood, but Bridget was always on the end of a phone to help him and his family through the 10-day detoxification period. By day six he experienced what are called 'user dreams' – vivid, colourful and very specific replays of drug-related activities. Day seven was spent staring at a tin can, shaking and hurting and wondering why he didn't just return to Bristol and, in his words, 'get off my face', but the other side of his head was telling him 'no', and by the ninth day he had a glimpse of a future. Darren has now begun a three-month treatment programme at a centre in Bournemouth – a daunting prospect for a drug user, as it demands a great deal of courage and commitment. I hope he succeeds.

Overall, the practice has an average success rate of 50 per cent in weaning drug users off drugs, and so, considering the investment of time, money and personal commitment, this can be a frustrating process. On the brighter side, it is always gratifying to meet an ex-addict who has returned to live a life free of chemical dependency.

Those that do break free have my sincere admiration. It is a long hard struggle to regain any quality of life. The lost years of addiction mean that the younger addicts have no qualifications and may not even have completed their schooling. The older ones will usually have no recent work experience and the blank years are not a good basis for convincing an employer that they are the employee he/she needs. The availability of support is vital, long after the initial dependency is controlled. I have great sympathy for those who have gone through the difficult detoxification programme, accepted their continuing addiction and resisted whichever substance they abused, only to find they cannot find a job or cannot afford to go back to college to get the basic qualifications they need. Often they find that as they come out of the fuzzy world of addiction they have nothing in common with their former 'user' friends and have been left far behind by their pre-addiction circle. It can be a very isolated position they find themselves in and those that succeed in coming through deserve credit for the strength of character that successful rehabilitation requires.

As a GP I am confronted almost on a daily basis with the effects of chemicals, both prescribed and unprescribed. As the father of four children I would have to be criminally disinterested not to realize that drugs are readily and cheaply available. Some of the youngsters I see in my surgery attended the same schools as my children. They had similar aspirations, they laughed at the same jokes, attended the same birthday parties, played rugby together, but at some time they said yes instead of no. No one can be complacent about the problem: it could be anybody's child. It may just take an adolescent sulk and a meeting with the wrong people. Add to that the availability of frighteningly addictive chemicals and another child is lost.

Fortunately for me at the age of 10, I was fully occupied fighting imaginary fires at Hestercombe House. Thirty years later I was at the same place, trying to learn how to fight an all-too-real holocaust that sadly endangers all our children.

15

Butlin's – Evening Surgery

It is my turn to do the evening surgery today at the Butlin's holiday centre and at 6.00 p.m., after a late start and a routine surgery at Irnham Lodge, it is quite relaxing to drive in through the main gate and sense the holiday mood. The evening surgery usually starts at 6.30 p.m. but Louise, who is the nursing sister in charge, phoned me during the afternoon and asked me to arrive earlier, as she was expecting a bigger surgery than usual.

For many people Minehead is almost synonymous with Butlin's and we are home to the largest of all the Butlin's holiday centres. When the camp is full in the summer there are around 8000 guests and 1500 staff, which almost equals the population of the town. The high street reflects this huge increase in the population during the holiday periods. Out of season Minehead is a quiet, rather sedate place, but in the summer it seems to come alive and the pavements and shops are overflowing with holidaymakers. Some local residents are in two minds as to whether Minehead needs Butlin's, but I have to say that while I rather like the calm at the end of the summer season, I am always pleased to see the bustling crowds return each year.

In 1964 when the camp opened, our predecessors in the practice were asked by Billy Butlin to provide the medical services, and our surgery has done so ever since. At first, the service was fairly limited, with patients being brought up to the surgery by bus and fitted into normal surgery times to see the doctors. As the numbers swelled it became too difficult to manage and arrangements were made to hold surgeries on the Butlin's premises, in the first-aid post. This was fine for a while but, again, as the numbers increased, the doctors could not cope with all the patients that needed to be seen. It was then that we started employing locum doctors to stay on camp, for a week or fortnight at a time, to provide the majority of the medical cover while we continued to take overall responsibility. We provide the accommodation, now in a mobile home by the lakeside, and the locum doctor moves in, usually with his or her family, for a working holiday. The family is able to use all the facilities of the centre while mum or dad does two surgeries a day and provides cover for emergencies. The system works very well and we have several regular locums who come back year after year, particularly while their families are young. We do surgeries twice a week to give the locum some time off and to cover the Saturday changeover day.

Over the last few years there has been considerable investment in the Butlin's holiday centre and recently we have heard that a further two-year redevelopment programme is planned. The medical centre, now upgraded from the original first-aid post, is well equipped with two consulting rooms, a treatment room and crash bay with all the necessary equipment, a good-sized waiting area and last year we proudly commissioned our own fully equipped ambulance. The centre is manned 24 hours a day by a team of six nurses, with Jess looking after the reception desk during the daytime. The busiest day we have ever had saw 184 patients through the door and the busiest week saw an incredible 1079 patients, but it is not always that bad!

The locum doctors are employed during the main busy summer holiday and Christmas seasons, and we take it in turns to attend surgeries at all other times and to cover the locum's time off. I must say that I enjoy it. Butlin's surgeries provide an interesting change in our style of consulting. Like any GP surgery you never know what is coming through the door next, and even more so here where you do not know any of the patients. The medical centre provides medical cover equivalent to any busy practice, but a surgery made up of holidaymakers has a different emphasis, both in respect of conditions presented and service required. The consultations tend to be brief. What the patient wants is quick attention for the problem they have so that they can get on with their holiday with the least possible delay. We don't, on the whole, have to be involved with their family dynamics and all the other things which are part of a usual GP consultation. It is rare to have to arrange a follow-up appointment.

People on holiday bring all their illnesses with them and, of course, manage to find new ones while they are away from home. We are well aware that becoming unwell while you are away from the safety of your own surroundings and not having your own doctor to call can be quite traumatic, so we seek to give the feel of a GP service rather than just emergency first-aid cover.

When I arrive at the medical centre, Louise greets me in her usual effusive style. She runs the centre with efficiency and enthusiasm and her larger-than-life personality brings a breath of fresh air to us all. She says what she thinks, knows what she wants and fights the medical centre's corner with a vengeance. This evening, Louise and her nurses are being kept particularly busy and, as well as a long surgery list, she also has a patient in the medical centre who is recovering from an epileptic attack and she wants me to see him before he is released. She has asked several patients to attend the evening surgery for further advice and my first two patients are lying on the beds in the emergency bay.

The first is Jenny, a young girl of 12, who is complaining of headache and some stiffness in her neck. She was brought in by her father 20 minutes ago after she fainted. Louise has checked her temperature and blood pressure, both of which are normal. She is looking very pale and quite sorry for herself. Headache and neck stiffness always raises the possibility of meningitis and though it is unlikely in this case, it is the first thing on my mind while I examine her. There has, quite rightly, been a lot of publicity about meningitis in recent years and Jenny's father brought her to us because he knew that neck stiffness can be a symptom.

Four years ago we had two cases of meningitis within 12 hours of each other at Butlin's. Both patients were holidaymakers, one a young girl of 18 and the other a two-year-old child. Their symptoms were recognized straight away by the locum doctor who gave them emergency treatment and admitted them immediately to Musgrove Hospital. The public health doctors sprang into action and I remember a midnight meeting in the medical centre to plan our course of action. The immediacy of the problem was that 5000 guests were due to be replaced by another 8000 in less than 48 hours' time and Butlin's needed to be advised as to what to do. With all the information available we could not establish a link between the two patients – their accommodation was well apart and neither had attended the same entertainment venues or dining facilities. We gave prophylactic antibiotic treatment to their respective families to prevent any infection occurring and advised Butlin's to continue with their usual Saturday changeover. The following morning the public health laboratory reported that the two patients were suffering different strains of the disease. This meant that the two cases

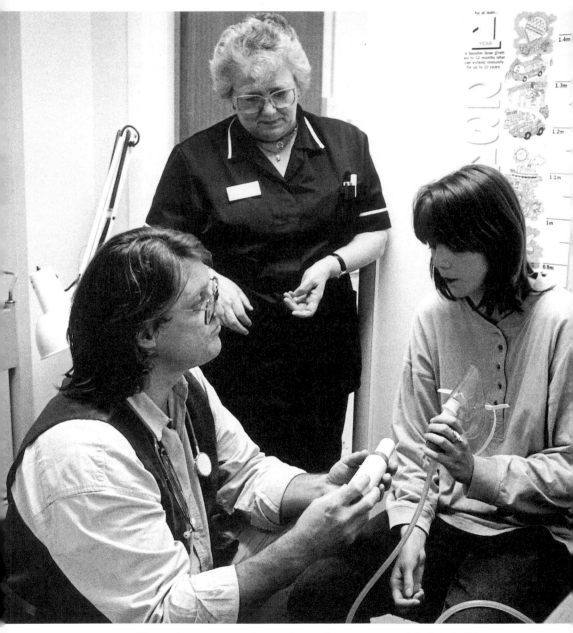

The patient wants quick attention so they can get on with their holiday.

occurring at the same time and at the same place were entirely coincidental – both had brought their meningitis with them and had not contracted it at Butlin's. This meant that we did not have an epidemic on our hands. However, by this time the 'meningitis scare' stories had been reported in the national newspapers and on TV and the telephone switchboard was hot with calls from would-be visitors and travel agents asking if it was safe to proceed with their holiday plans.

We decided to make contact with the Meningitis Trust. In circumstances like these I think that people are doubtful of statements from authorities – there can be an understandable suspicion and a feeling that something may be being hidden – particularly when the proclamations are of the reassuring sort. Lay organizations, who have no axe to grind, are far more likely to be seen as trustworthy and the Trust's response was terrific. It provided the reassurance that the holidaymakers wanted by manning the telephone enquiry line and by greeting guests, as they arrived at the gates on the Saturday morning, with explanatory leaflets. The success of this programme of information can be seen by the fact that we were expecting a lot of worried patients during the following week, but there were actually no more than usual. Tragically, the young girl died although, thankfully, the two-year-old did make a full recovery, and, fortunately, no other cases occurred. When an otherwise healthy youngster can die so suddenly it is very understandable that people are worried when they are presented with symptoms similar to those of meningitis.

My examination of Jenny certainly shows no indication of meningitis. In fact, I can't find anything particularly wrong apart from some signs of mild dehydration. Further discussion with her dad reveals that she had missed her lunch and she has spent a hot afternoon jumping up and down at a Redcoat show. My best medical advice is a paracetamol and a pint of orange squash – she will be fine.

The other patient in the emergency bay is James, a 22-year-old member of staff, who has had an epileptic fit. James works in customer catering as a kitchen hand. He came down to work at Butlin's eight weeks ago and he has had two fits during that time. He has been epileptic for six years and is on a complicated mixture of medication prescribed by his consultant in Liverpool. He had been free of fits for over a year and had decided, as he was so well, to cut back on his tablets. That, as well as the irregular and long hours he is working, has tipped the scales and allowed the fits to return. Although he has a headache he is now recovered well enough to go back to his room to rest. He agrees to go back on to his full dose and I have arranged to see him at Irnham Lodge in a week's time. His past

GP medical records, with the letters from his consultant, will have arrived by then and I will be in a much better position to advise him. If he is not well enough for work he will return to the medical centre for a 24-hour sick note.

It is now time to tackle the ever-increasing crowd in the waiting room. As patients arrive at the medical centre they book in at reception and some temporary record cards are made up and put in a box by the consulting-room door. I take the heap of cards and get stuck in. Rashes, earaches, belly aches and sore throats all come through the door and are dealt with as expeditiously as possible, though I am constantly on the look-out for anything unusual – is this a simple colic or the first signs of an appendicitis? After an hour I have seen 14 patients but the waiting room is no emptier – just full of different faces. Each time I call a new patient there are more record cards in the box by the door. I am beginning to feel like the frog trying to get out of the well – one brick up and two down.

The surgery continues. A wasp sting, a twisted ankle following an over-enthusiastic boogie in one of the discos; most are straightforward and patients only need reassurance and advice. The best ones are those who apologetically ask for a repeat prescription.

'I am sorry Doctor, but I said to my wife, "The last thing I must forget are my heart pills" – and the last thing I managed to forget was my heart pills.'

The remaining patients include children with an upper respiratory infection, a throat infection and ear infections. These are easily dealt with, enabling children and parents to continue enjoying their holiday. Finally, I see an elderly man from Wales, a retired coal miner, who comes in from the waiting room accompanied by his wife. He is very breathless and flushed and the effort of walking the few paces from the chair in the waiting room has left him unable to speak. His wife tells me that he has a history of chronic bronchitis and emphysema and also suffers from angina and then she empties a carrier-bag of medications onto my desk. He is using three different inhalers for his chest and has a collection of six more medications in tablet form for his heart disease and other symptoms such as night cramps. He clearly has an acute chest infection, a situation that he is quite used to. After I have examined him and his breath is recovered he tells me that he has been trying to ignore his worsening condition in the hope that he would improve on his own. He didn't want to make a fuss and ruin the family holiday. I arrange for Louise to put him on the nebulizer and within 10 minutes his breathing is a lot easier. The nebulizer is an electric pump that blows air through a bronchodilator solution, turning it into a very fine mist which is easily absorbed when breathed in through the lungs. The bronchodilator medication relaxes the muscles in the tubing of the lungs and eases the tightness of the asthma. He clearly is in no condition to be cared for in holiday accommodation and, after checking that we have a bed spare, I offer to take him in to Minehead Hospital. It is a great relief to him and his family that he can be treated in our local cottage hospital. It means that he will get the care he needs, but his family can continue their holiday and be able to pop in and see him throughout the day.

I like to think that our commitment to the medical centre and Butlin's means that the usual minor ailments and injuries remain minor, both physically and emotionally. Statistically, with such a large transient population, there is always bound to be a certain level of ill health and injuries, but these, if treated promptly, need not become an issue which detracts from the purpose of the trip to Minehead – to have a good time. At the end of the surgery I have seen 18 patients. It has taken me an hour and a half and I feel I have had enough for now.

As I drive out of Butlin's the go-karts are whizzing round, couples and families are strolling off to their evening meal or heading for the various shows, discos and clubs at the centre. Unfortunately for me, it is a night on call. I will drop my patient off at the hospital and sort out his paperwork and medications. I can then head on home and, hopefully, will be able to eat my dinner before the dreaded bleep has me bumping down my drive again. Roll on eight o' clock tomorrow morning when someone else takes over.

16

Biddely-beep

It hadn't occurred to me when we agreed to take part in the television series that the crew would also want to film in the bedroom during night shifts. I'd come to terms with the fact that my life for the next six months would be shared with a producer, a cameraman and a sound recordist, and that they'd be following me around sheep like while I went about my daily work routine – surgery, home visits and casualty duties. But the thought had never crossed my mind that even my sleeping pattern would be disturbed. While sharing my anxieties with Huw – who was also to undergo this invasion of privacy – we discovered a major setback. We didn't own a single pair of pyjamas between us. After a brief discussion we decided it would be a legitimate practice expense to purchase a pair.

'They have to be paisley,' Huw insisted. I can't say I've ever given the design of night attire much thought, but Huw was adamant. After all, he'd been keeping abreast of the medical dramas currently being shown on our TV channels.

'I know in ER they wear theatre greens in bed,' he sighed, 'but no one will believe we've had 30 years experience between us if we show up wearing those. Anyway, I've always felt my life has been a little deprived because I didn't own a pair of paisley pyjamas.' Poor Huwie.

Now, in a place like Minehead a paisley pyjama is hard to find, unless of course you're paying a visit to an elderly gentleman on the surgical ward of Minehead Hospital. There, paisley is definitely in vogue. But try to buy yourself a pair and you're faced with all kinds of excuses. 'Sorry, sir, we sold the last pair yesterday,' and, 'Oh no, they went out of fashion a long while back.' (Since when has Minehead been a setter of trends, I wondered?) Instead, armed with the practice petty-cash purse, I ventured into Best Buy and emerged just three minutes later with a very fetching maroon stripe. Huwie was distraught.

My first night shift was looming and I couldn't imagine my wife, Anne, ever letting a camera crew anywhere near the marital bed. I eventually plucked up the courage to raise the subject and, after

A visit to little Tom at home was just part of my busy night duty.

much discussion with the producer, we reached a compromise. A small camera would be rigged in the bedroom with a remote control that I could operate from my bedside table and the shot would be framed to exclude Anne on the other side of the bed, thus eliminating the presence of two bleary-eyed technicians at the foot of our bed at 3.00 a.m. There was an added complication. Because we have no mains electricity at the farm, I would also have to throw a switch to trigger the generator into action in order to provide enough light to produce an image for the camera. Not only that, but having gone through this procedure, I would then have to turn off the light, pretend I was asleep and then react spontaneously to the sound of my bleep, which includes reading the message and making the necessary phone call. We rehearsed several times during the course of the evening and I thought I'd got the hang of it.

The dreaded night arrived and, after a busy evening in casualty, I prepared myself for bed. But where were the maroon-striped pyjamas? A desperate search began and, after much cussing and swearing, I traced them to the boot of the MG, neatly spliced between the week's supply of pig food and the spare tyre. Unravelling them from their polythene wrapper, I realized there would be no mistaking them as the brand new, perfectly pressed pair of pyjamas they were, complete with identical folds running down each side of the jacket.

It wasn't the bleep that woke me at 1.15 a.m., but the dressmaker's pins that had been securing the pyjamas to their cardboard stiffener. When the bleep did eventually go off at 2.35 a.m. it was, rather ironically, a call from the police station asking if I could administer a sleeping pill to a detainee in one of the cells. As police surgeons for Minehead police station, we are called around a hundred times a year to deal with the medical needs of people detained in the police cells. This can often involve judging whether someone is fit for detention or for being interviewed by the police officers and, in drink-driving cases, taking blood and alcohol tests. Fifty per cent of these calls are at night and so add an extra burden to our out-of-hours duties.

Even without the addition of a remote-controlled camera in the bedroom, sleeping when you are on call is always different to sleeping when you are off duty. In the latter case your snores disturb others for miles around while you remain oblivious to the world's cares and dream pleasantly about playing rugby with the Spice Girls. In on-call mode you experience a lighter pattern when even the slightest noise can have you grabbing for the telephone receiver before it rings and wakes the whole family. It must be the kind of sleep that our ancestors had to put up with night after night, their subconscious alert to the possibility of attack by a wild animal or a warring tribal neighbour.

Any doctor who has been through the uncertain and certain agonies of being a junior hospital doctor on call for the first time could tell you of the harrowing imprint this experience leaves on the psyche. There develops a Pavlovian conditioned response to *that noise*, the dreaded siren-call to action, the blasted bleep.

The Junior Hospital Doctor:

Biddely-beep, biddely-beep.'Your groping hand knocks your bedside glass off its roost, its contents soaking the sheet. Fumble for the light switch, anxiety mounting. What is it this time? A life or death emergency or something less urgent, but still requiring immediate response? Will I be able to cope on my own? At all costs, stop the bloody bleep making that god-awful sound. Hit the button. Phone the ward. Please God, don't let it be Mrs Thompson's drip tissuing again. It took me half an hour to get the last one running freely, and I used her last remaining vein. The only one left in her whole damn body. Please God, not Mrs Thompson's drip.

'Mrs Thompson's drip has tissued, doctor. The fluid is running into her arm and making it swollen. Can you come and re-site it please?'

The fight-and-flight dread at the moment of being abruptly woken by 'biddely-beep' remains even as you approach the comfortable coalescing zones of middle age and experience. Nothing changes.

The General Practitioner:

Biddely-beep, biddely-beep. Your groping hand knocks your bedside glass off its roost, its contents soaking the sheet, dentures falling into the fluff behind the bedhead. Fumble for the light switch, anxiety mounting. What is it this time? You'd think that after all these years I'd be used to this.

As a hospital doctor, you know that the patient will have previously been seen by either a nurse or their GP and there is no question that the call-out is necessary, but as a GP you are the first point of contact with the patient. The first thought for the GP is, 'Does this call require me to see the patient straightaway or can I give some advice and sort it out in the morning?' Some are straightforward – chest pain, breathlessness, diabetic collapse, a caller in obvious distress – a few details taken and you roll out of bed, jam on some easy clothing and get going. (When one neighbouring GP first started, he was renowned for arriving at the patient's home or the casualty department in the middle of the night as though he had been invited to dinner – creaseless shirt and natty matching tie, jacket and neatly pressed trousers. After a while his standards, disappointingly, slipped and though he still polishes his shoes before leaving his front door, he has dispensed with the tie.) The more difficult judgements are the non-specific illnesses – the belly ache is most likely to be a tummy bug, but could it be an appendicitis or

An early evening call to Withycombe village.

bowel obstruction? The child with a temperature – most likely to be a feverish cold, but could it be meningitis? These are the ones that find us questioning the caller and this sometimes gets misinterpreted as a reluctance to respond immediately.

After discussing the situation, I like to invite the patient or relative to make the decision as to whether I attend or not – after all, they are on the spot and know how concerned they are. I had a standard question at the end of a doubtful 'visit or not' call. At midnight one night I used my usual line on a young mother – 'What would *you* like me to do?' – meaning, 'Do you want me to visit or are you happy to take my advice and get him checked tomorrow?' It was interpreted as 'What would you like *me* to do about it?' meaning, 'Why the hell are you bothering me?' She went ballistic for two minutes, and, before I could get a word in, slammed the phone down. I rang back immediately to find the engaged tone and decided to visit to sort things out. Before I finished my quick-change act to no audience, both the casualty department and ambulance service had phoned to query the validity of an emergency call they had received, which included threats of litigation and vile doings to the emergency doctor. I phoned again and got through to the husband who told me, 'The kiddie's a bit hot, but he doesn't seem too bad.' I went anyway. When I arrived at their home the bewildered child was sitting happily on his father's knee, mother was in the bedroom and would not come down to talk, and both father and child looked as though they needed to get back to bed – like me.

My new line, having assessed the situation, is to say, in my softest and most comforting tone, 'From what you tell me, I don't think I need to call tonight, but will be happy to see you in surgery tomorrow morning. Do you think there is the need for an emergency visit?' More often than not, the decision is to wait and see. I offer advice to call again if they become concerned and the caller is reassured, while I can confidently return to my dreams of the rugby changing room.

The vast majority of night-time calls are genuine and I find my patients are considerate and needlessly apologetic when they have to call during the night. However, there are always the exceptions, and as a GP of 20 years it is hard to fathom the thought processes of some people whose definitions of 'urgent' and 'serious enough to wake the doctor for' seem at variance with any dictionary or reference book that has ever been published. Colleagues and I have experienced the following:

2.30 a.m. *Biddely-beep, biddely-beep.*
Operator: 'Doctor, will you accept a reverse charge call?'
Doctor: 'I suppose I better had.'
Patient: 'I'm on holiday from Birmingham and I've just finished cleaning the oven with oven cleaner. I'm now reading the tin, which says I should have been wearing gloves. My hands seem all right, but what should I do?'

3.30 a.m. *Biddely-beep, biddely-beep.* 'Doctor, my arm's hurting like mad in this sling and I can't open the bottle of painkillers. It's just that I don't want to wake the neighbours.'

4.30 a.m. *Biddely-beep, biddely-beep.* 'I've just told my boyfriend that if he doesn't leave his wife I'll kill myself. He's told me that he thinks that would be a good idea. What shall I do?'

5.30 a.m. *Biddely-beep, biddely-beep.* 'I want to call a taxi and I don't have a phone book. I knew you'd be awake. Can you give me the number for a cab?'

Come back, Mrs Thompson, all is forgiven.

17

Bad News

While on duty in the casualty department a couple of weeks ago, I was called to the ward sister's office to discuss a patient of Liz's who has been in Minehead Hospital for the past few weeks. Her husband Brian is a patient of mine – a delightful Yorkshireman who works as an RSPCA inspector at Taunton market. As well as seeing him occasionally in surgery, we sometimes bump into each other on my annual visit to the market in the autumn when I sell my pigs. He came to see me in the surgery a few days ago, suffering from the stress of caring for his wife, who is in the terminal stages of cancer. They are a truly devoted couple and Brian spends nearly every hour of each day at Joan's bedside.

I discussed her condition with Del, the nurse, and it was clear that Joan was rapidly deteriorating and exhausted. Brian had been harbouring a glimmer of hope that Joan might improve and may even come home to him again, but I knew it was time to tell him that we had to accept the inevitability of her illness. I don't enjoy this side of my job, and I knew it would be a difficult conversation for both of us. But during my time as a GP I have learned that it is best to switch off your own personal feelings, and, instead, think of the emotions of the patient. I explained to Brian that if we gave her something to relax her breathing it might actually hasten the end. I knew he had been dreading this moment and I feared for him as I explained the alternatives, but it had to be as much his decision as mine. We agreed that our aim would be to keep her comfortable and alleviate any pain or distress. He was then silent and I asked if there was anything more he'd like to know. He shook his head: 'I'd just like to get back to Joan.' As I left him in the corridor, he wiped away a tear before returning to her bedside.

When I trained to be a doctor over a quarter of a century ago there were no lectures on counselling, no interactive video training programmes on how to break the news that a loved one was dying or

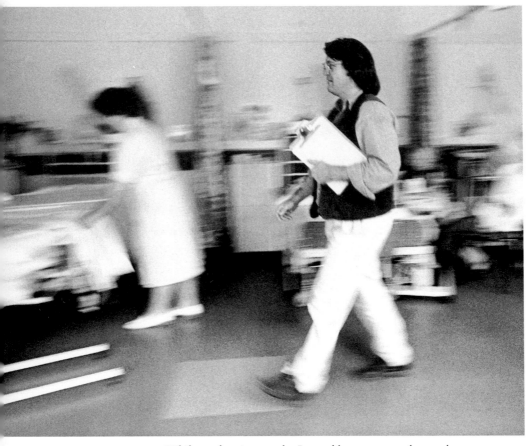

While on duty in casualty I am able to go up to the wards to check on my in-patients.

had died. It was rather assumed that if you were a 'decent enough chap' you would do it perfectly well, and, anyway, we were dealing with diagnosis and treatment, and if a patient died that was the end of it. You learned by doing it. It was a hard way of learning; hard for you and much harder for the poor relative who came to realize, via your clumsy embarrassed efforts, that something untoward had happened that was going to change their life.

Having been a general practitioner for 20 years I cannot recall any more all the countless times that I have had to break bad news. The last few, yes, but most of the others blur into an amorphous recollection that makes them storable in a way that enables you to carry on functioning. It may sound callous, but it's practical. You soon have to learn that you cannot carry all your patients' grief around with you, but as a young doctor you inevitably make the mistake of trying to.

Although all doctors are supposed to possess the same qualities, we all handle things in our own different ways, all make our own different mistakes. The story of the sergeant major giving bad news to a member of his squad comes to mind: 'All those with a living mother at home take two steps forward ... Hold it, hold it ... where do you think you are going, Jones?'

There could have been a slightly more tactful, not to mention private, way of breaking the news to Corporal Jones that his mother had died, but bad news is bad news and the way you learn it can't really make any difference, can it? The truth is that it does matter, and if a doctor doesn't think so, then he or she is in the wrong job.

Having said that the episodes of bad-news-breaking fade in the memory, that is not true of the first time you are faced with the awfulness of it. We all remember our first encounters and experiences, good and bad. First sexual encounter, first alcoholic stupor, first try at rugby (and it was only the partially sighted ref. that allowed me to get away with that one).

In my first week of being a fully registered doctor I was working in casualty. After a busy six months as a pre-registration house officer in general medicine I knew how to handle a medical emergency, though with the extra responsibility of being a senior house officer, I felt a little like a small boat bobbing about in the English Channel and heading out towards the Atlantic. A young man was brought by ambulance to casualty, having collapsed while playing hockey. The crash button was pressed and the duty emergency team materialized in moments.

We continued the cardio-pulmonary resuscitation as we transferred him from the ambulance into the emergency room, but from the start his fixed dilated pupils told us that he was already dead. His ECG (electrocardiogram) monitor showed no sign of activity and, after trying all the bring-back-to-life tricks, there was no response. We looked at each other and agreed that any further attempts at treatment were futile, and he was officially declared dead. The anaesthetist and medical team went back to their other duties and I returned to the cuts and bruises sitting in the waiting room.

The young man's mother came into casualty a short time later. The sister in charge who would have normally taken control of the situation had left the department to escort an admission patient to the ward and the other nurses were busy with patients. The clerk introduced me as the doctor in charge and left me with a smiling if somewhat exasperated woman who was under the impression that she was about to collect her suitably bandaged sporting son. I didn't

Giving someone bad news is an inevitable part of a family doctor's work.

have a clue what to say. I asked her to come to a quiet side room and she followed me, still smiling.

'I'm sorry Mrs M, I'm afraid Tony is dead.'

No preamble, no warning sign that I was going give her some news from which she would never fully recover. On reflection, I realized that the look she gave me was probably one of disbelief, but at the time I thought it was a look of pure hatred directed at me. Now, 20 years on, my main concern would be for her feelings, her loss, her pain, and her bewildered disbelief. Then, I could not get past my pain at having to face this mother, my loss of a patient and my bewildered disbelief that I was in this awful position. I did not know what to say next. Fortunately for me, and much more fortunately for Tony's mother the sister in charge came into the room and, quickly assessing the situation, told me I was urgently needed elsewhere and gently steered Tony's mother to a chair and a more compassionate explanation. I had difficulty seeing where I was walking as I left the room and felt that I, too, needed someone to gently steer me towards a chair.

I thought long and hard about how I should have handled that interview. I needed to be better prepared for the situation. I needed to better prepare the relative for the news and, having given the news, I needed to be prepared to cope and, for a while, share their grief. There is no getting away from the message that needs to be imparted, but allowing someone a few seconds to adjust their expectations as to what they are going to hear does help. An empathetic rather than a sympathetic attitude can help both relative and doctor. It is their grief, not mine, but how would I like to be treated in that situation?

Giving someone bad news is an inevitable part of a family doctor's work and if it is handled badly it not only hurts the grieving relative, but the doctor can end up on the fast track to a detached and cynical working persona, which is both professionally and personally damaging. Fortunately, experience teaches that there are helpful and empathetic ways of imparting bad news and, as with any job, done well can have its rewards.

Joan died in Minehead Hospital a week after my talk with her husband. She was comfortable and he was at her side. I paid a visit to Brian at home shortly after the funeral, mostly to show that we hadn't forgotten him and that we were always there if he needed us. He wanted to show me some photographs of Joan before she became ill and I took great delight in sharing some of the happy memories he recounted. Brian is an active man and I'm sure that before long he'll be able to get on with his life again. I shall look forward to seeing him at Taunton market in the autumn.

18

Daff

In the top corner of the seven-acre field there is a young purple beech tree. Despite the post and wire protection, one of the larger deer has managed to reach over the top and bite off the main leader shoot. In 20 years' time the tree will be big and strong and its odd shape may be noticed by picnickers and fishermen passing in boats. That would amuse Daff – the new spring buds are nourished by his ashes.

In the course of a lifetime's career in general practice, there are patients and incidents that have a dramatic effect on your life. I make no apologies for relating this story to you in every detail, as for the past six years it has been a constant reminder of how my work can touch every nerve-end and every emotion I possess. The story of Daff's short life is one I will never, ever forget.

Daff had been a contemporary of my own children through school, and I had known him as an occasional patient for several years when, in 1991, at the age of 19, he came to show me a swelling on his right forearm. He thought he must have strained a muscle somehow. It wasn't particularly painful, but it had been there for some time and he wondered whether there was anything that could be done to settle it down. I felt his arm, and as my fingers gently explored the swelling, it was clear that Daff was in for a tough time. I had come across something similar in a patient as a junior hospital doctor in the oncology department at Canterbury Hospital. I was pretty certain that this was a tumour, but what I needed to know was whether it was benign or malignant – I strongly suspected the latter.

It is difficult to describe the mixture of feelings that you get when you know you have found a potentially serious disease. You have a professional sense of interest, even excitement that you have found something out of the ordinary, but on the other hand, you feel a mixture of concern and anxiety for the patient, particularly when the patient is so young. I arranged for Daff to be seen promptly by our local orthopaedic surgeon, who soon took him into hospital for a biopsy. In a few days I was disappointed to learn that he had a tumour known as a sarcoma. This was certainly no muscle strain.

Daff – whose real name was Matthew – had been given his nickname by his art teacher at Dulverton School because he was fond of drawing pictures of Daffy Duck. He lived with his mother, Gill, and sister, Rebecca, in a house that was always full of friends and vitality. He was tall and thin and liked to wear his hair long and his clothing colourful and loose. He was vegetarian and he liked his Guinness. He was a young man full of life – in fact, a character.

On the same day that I received the biopsy report Gill phoned me. She told me that after the biopsy operation the young doctor on the orthopaedic team had taken her to one side. He had told her that Daff had cancer but had advised that it would be better not tell him the news just yet and they would be in touch. That was all she could remember. She had probably been told more, but all she could recall was that she felt her insides had been dragged from within her. She had driven Daff home thinking of nothing else but talking of anything and everything else. Gill decided to follow the advice from Bristol and had told Daff nothing. However, the next time the hospital got in touch it was to write with an appointment for him to go for radiotherapy treatment. Gill didn't know what to do and phoned me for help. I remember driving up to their house in Church Street in Alcombe with a sense of dread, planning how to break the news. The house was full of people, but they quickly dispersed and left me with Gill and Daff. We talked around the subjects of growths and tumours, the nature of malignancy, the significance of the disease and the importance of treatment. Daff didn't take it in. He was 19. He knew that he was immortal and invincible. To him it wasn't life-threatening – you don't die at the age of 19. His mother confirmed this when she told me the story of him lying in the middle of the road, after a few jars of Guinness, to see if the pizza van would hit him. It didn't, and that confirmed to him that he was a survivor. We talked for a long time and slowly the cruel diagnosis was understood, if not accepted. When I left his house that afternoon it was with a very heavy heart but Daff was already showing the spirit that was to help not only him but all of us who shared his last months. Clearly, it would take time for him to fully comprehend the news, but by the time I left his main concern was for Gill and Rebecca rather than himself.

Next time I saw him, Daff wanted all treatment options explained to him. He agreed to undergo radiotherapy directed at the tumour in his arm, believing that this was a holistic approach. Chemotherapy was not for him – he thought it was too intrusive, 'destroying the good stuff in your body as well as the bad'. Over the following months Daff had several courses of radiotherapy which succeeded in shrinking the tumour but left him with radiation burns to the skin. Fortunately, the burns responded well to homeopathic treatment. His fierce independence asserted itself and he insisted on travelling alone to Bristol for his treatment, a round trip of 130 miles. He would accept a lift to Taunton station and then take the train and bus to the hospital. On the return journey he would hitchhike the 26 miles from Taunton to Minehead – I remember seeing him thumbing a lift and picking him up as I drove back from a school run.

A friend gave Daff the address of the Bristol Cancer Centre. He made contact with them and in July 1992 he went to them for a week of residential care. He was accompanied by a long-time family friend and 'surrogate aunt' Dot Lupo, who went as his companion – someone who could learn alongside him and support him on his return home. Among other things, he was taught to visualize his disease and this, and the overall approach of informed support, helped Daff to return from his stay at the Centre with a positive while still realistic outlook. He continued to make the most of each day and around this time he took up painting and drawing again. Some months after his death Gill gave me one of his pictures which I have, framed, on my consulting-room wall.

Daff became vegan and started taking extra vitamins and dietary supplements, which I was pleased to be able to prescribe for him. The medications were important, but, just as importantly, it gave us an opportunity to meet regularly, to talk and review progress and setbacks, and to plan our next step. He continued with regular checks in Bristol and at one point chemotherapy was reconsidered. As a matter of routine he was advised to have some sperm frozen – chemotherapy sometimes causes sterility, and as a young man he might in the future wish to have children. Gill remembers the hospital visit well. 'He was given a specimen bottle and pointed in the direction of a toilet. It was really humiliating for Daff but he just got on with it.' When he reappeared he put the semen in his pocket to keep it warm, and walked as quickly as he could across the hospital grounds to the sperm bank where it would be frozen. Gill's sense of humour never faltered and she called after him, 'You be careful, you've got my grandchildren in there!'

Throughout this time he managed to maintain his optimism and generally regarded the illness as a nuisance which, in particular, was interfering with his plans to go travelling with his best friend, Charlie. Of course there were bad days and for a short period of time he sought solace from an excess of Guinness. However, towards the end of 1992 one of the girls in his circle of friends broke up with her boyfriend. Justine and Daff became very close and within a few weeks Daff had moved out of the family house to live with her. Justine was fully aware of his illness, but they were a perfect match and it was the start of a relationship that enriched both their lives. They became inseparable, cycling everywhere and indulging in retail therapy, which involved going to the shops to buy ridiculous, cheap items for their home. I continued to see Daff regularly in surgery and then in the spring of 1993, a year after his first diagnosis, I had a phone call from Dr Jill Bullimore, his Bristol oncologist. She told me that they had found secondary cancer spreading in his lungs. She could offer local radiotherapy to try to alleviate any symptoms of breathlessness, but we both knew that this was the beginning of the end for Daff.

As usual, he seemed to take the news calmly, making out that he regarded it only as a setback, and then set about planning a trip to India, which was a long-held ambition. I knew that the trip was quite impossible, and without saying so he knew it too, but we went through almost a game of working out what vaccinations and what type of malarial protection he and Justine would need. Over the next few weeks Daff gradually became thinner and more breathless with the least exertion and when they discussed their plans with Dr Bullimore she told them, 'If you have to go then go, but, Justine, you will have to deal with everything if Daff becomes ill.' In the end, they both accepted that they could not place that responsibility on Justine and instead they spent a long weekend in Paris. Soon after their return they came to see me together and told me that they planned to marry. The bravery of those two young people, in such a state of adversity, making plans for the future – laughing and smiling – is something I shall never forget. I admired and loved them for it.

They married a few months later, in July, travelling to the Williton Register Office in Charlie's father's open-topped Alvis. They wore clothes that Justine had made for the occasion, buying the materials on another retail therapy trip to Exeter. A green velvet suit for her and a ridiculous pair of multi-coloured clown's trousers and braces for him. In the weeks leading up to their wedding, Justine had to keep altering the trousers because of his increasing weight loss but, despite his weakening condition, Daff managed to keep going all through the wedding day so as not to let his friends and family down. Justine told me, 'He was exhausted, but spent the day beaming his lopsided cheesy grin.'

The honeymoon was not such a success. Gill had paid for them to have a barge holiday on the canals around Oxford. It had always been a dream of Daff's to live on a barge and this was the next best thing. By the second day of the honeymoon Daff's breathing had become extremely laboured and he was simply too weak. Justine could not manage the boat and look after Daff at the same time and so she found a phone box and called me in surgery to tell me what was happening. I reluctantly advised them to return home. I called Gill, who rescued them from the river and brought them back to Minehead. Daff was relieved to be home.

By August Daff was getting repeated chest infections and I knew that we were moving to the terminal stages of his disease. Most GP surgeries have a large number of support staff and there are many agencies that we can call upon for help. Kay Cheeseman is the community support nurse from our local hospice, St Margaret's, in Taunton. Perhaps due to the intensity of the situations that bring us together I have a particularly close relationship with her. I had been keeping Kay informed throughout Daff's illness and we had decided that because of his approach it had not been appropriate for her to be directly involved. However, the time had come when he needed a professional friend to see him through. Daff was reluctant at first to meet her. Kay is sometimes seen as the Grim Reaper's sidekick – an image at odds with that of her driving wildly around town in a bright yellow, open-topped Morgan sports car. Happily, at the first meeting they hit it off immediately.

His strength continued to decline and some time later he confided in Justine that he couldn't cope any more. She came to see me and we had a frank talk about the reality of the situation and what she should expect in the coming few weeks. She has since told me that she was relieved to know the truth about what she was facing.

Just as he was vital in life, Daff brought vitality to the preparations for his coming death. He had never kept a diary in his life, but now he made lists of events and things to do in a Filofax, which he

To this day Daff's friends still come up and sit on the log by the tree.

insisted Justine get for him, along with an alarm clock to satisfy his sudden interest in time. Daff went around the house with his tray of important belongings – personal stereo, fag-making equipment, lighter, nebulizer and the alarm clock, which he constantly checked. Gill and Justine described him as a Maharajah, sitting on large, soft, colourful cushions, with his harem in constant attention. Everything had to be put in order, and he made arrangements for his dad, Nigel – whom he had not seen for many years – to visit. He invited his friends around to ask them if they would be his gravediggers and made a list of those who agreed. He didn't want to die until he had sorted out his burial, but quickly discovered that it was not quite legal to get your friends to dig any old hole and bung you in it, which was his first idea. He decided on cremation and a memorial. After studying the tree catalogues and pictures he settled for the purple beech. The family made plans for the memorial tree to be planted in the area of Culbone, near Porlock. Culbone church, which is the smallest in England, is inaccessible by road and a very quiet and peaceful place. Charlie was away in South Africa and a message was sent to him that Daff was nearing the end. He caught a flight home and made it with three days to spare.

Kay became, as usual, a vital support to us all. She visited frequently and would report back to me. It is not uncommon for patients to say things to nurses that they are reluctant – for all sorts of reasons – to tell doctors, and I was able to call in every three or four days armed with the details of the latest situation concerning his breathing problems and pain relief. Justine was becoming exhausted and Kay and I persuaded Daff to go into the hospice for a few days. It gave Justine a break and also settled some of his breathing difficulties. He would only stay for 24 hours, as he was terrified of dying there, but the break did them all some good. He came home to a house which was a warm, secure and happy place. The children who normally played noisily outside fell quiet. Justine remembers, 'It was so peaceful it felt like it had a bubble around it.'

We moved him upstairs to bed for the last few days, Gill and Justine spending alternate nights by his side – with Daff throwing shoes and anything else to hand at Gill to stop her from snoring and keeping him awake. He tidied his final loose ends. He spoke to Gill and, for the first time since his early childhood, started calling her Mum. He spoke to Justine, to Rebecca and to his friends. He asked me to visit so that he could thank me for what I had done for him and to tell me that he loved me.

His family encouraged him to have something delicious to eat – he had been introducing some of his favourite foods into his vegan diet over the last few months and they thought he would like some cheese – but what he really craved for was chips and tomato sauce. Gill's partner, Jim, went down to the fish and chip shop and brought back four portions of chips. While they could only pick at their meal, Daff tucked in like a trencherman, and after he had finished his own plateful he cleared the rest of the plates. From then on he sat upright in bed and drifted in and out of sleep. In his times of wakefulness he said very little. Justine remembers, 'He wouldn't lie down, he just sat upright, staring at me with his piercing blue eyes.' On the Sunday night he seemed to stop breathing several times and when he awoke in the morning he told his mum that he had seen a very bright light and a man called Albert who had a dog with him. Albert had asked him to come away but Daff had hesitated. Albert could not wait and left without him.

Kay and I were at the house on and off through the following day, adjusting his medication and ensuring that he was comfortable, and at 7.20 p.m. on Monday 12 September, surrounded by those he loved, Daff stopped breathing for the last time. Perhaps Albert and his dog had returned and taken Daff with them.

After the funeral and cremation, arrangements were made to plant the beech tree, and on a cold, wet morning a small party of friends and family carried the tree across the fields to the church. With the trustees' agreement the tree was planted along with Daff's ashes in the lawn by the church. Unfortunately, some time later there was a change of heart, as it was considered that the tree was too near a wall which would become damaged by the growing roots. In order to save any fuss, Gill arranged for the tree to be dug up and put in a large pot, which she then kept by her back door. I knew nothing of these difficulties until Justine came to see me in surgery, and during our conversation I learned that the tree, and Daff, still had no final resting place. I told her about the corner of the seven-acre field and she thought that it would be ideal. Daff had often walked through the farm on visits to an old ruined chapel beyond, and knew the area well. She felt that he would like his tree to be looking out to sea. A couple of weeks later the same group of family and friends turned up with spades and picks, and the tree in its tub. We chose the spot, planted the tree and then consumed Guinness and red wine while we remembered him. Gill and Justine visit regularly, particularly on birthdays and anniversaries, and to this day his friends still come up and sit on the log by his tree. It has become part of the tradition to drink half a can of Guinness and to pour the rest around the roots of the tree – what better way to celebrate the life of a really great guy than to feel you can still raise a can and share a drink with him.

Daff's death reaffirmed my view that doctors and nurses are in a privileged position to be asked into people's lives at times of great crisis and joy. Tears were shed by everyone involved with the care of Daff but because of his spirit and personality he enabled us all to take something positive from sharing with him and his family his last two years. I know that Kay and I, and all the district nurses who worked so hard for him, felt a sense of fulfilment and satisfaction at a job well done. We could not cure him or prevent all the side-effects to his treatment. We could not take away the pain felt by his family and friends. It might seem easier to become very 'professional' and try to detach emotionally from the situation, but experience has shown me that while it is emotionally draining to become involved, it is also emotionally healing. While I have shed a tear recalling Daff's death for this book, the lasting impression is positive. Daff loved and was loved. He and his family met death with great regret but enormous dignity. It seems to me that the way we meet death will not make any difference to the amount we miss those that die or lessen the grief, but it can take something of the 'sting' out of death's tail. I know that I look back on the death of some patients and see only grief, whereas when I look back on Daff's death, I see only Daff.

19

End of the Day

It's Friday evening and, with the last surgery of the week over, I have a weekend off duty to look forward to a visit from my daughter and her family. It has been a busy week and the prospect of getting to know my new granddaughter, playing cars, stamping in rock pools on the beach and generally entering the world of my 22-month-old grandson is very appealing. It is lovely to return to seeing the world through a young child's eyes. Instead of sighing at the delay when the level crossing lights flash, I drive slowly approaching the crossing, in the hope that Jakey will be able to see the steam train. Instead of resolving to repair our potholed drive, I rush out to splash in the puddles, although Jake's yellow wellies are unable to withstand his splashing zeal. Every boat that passes the farm is of interest, we 'moo' at the cows, 'baa' at the sheep and 'oink' at the pigs. For Jake and Imogen, everything is new and interesting and a toddler's unflagging interest and uncomplicated enthusiasm is wonderfully infectious. An hour in their company is the perfect prescription for winding down and getting things into perspective.

The surgery has been a long one and I have two visits to make before I can head for home. The first is to an elderly man in a residential home. I have not met him before as he only moved to Minehead two days ago, following the death of his wife. They had been married for over 40 years and had spent the majority of their time in the Williton area. Three years ago George suffered a stroke that left him speechless and with a right-sided paralysis. With the help of his wife he made a very good recovery. Sadly, she became ill two months ago and needed to be admitted to Williton Hospital for terminal care. George was also admitted, as he could not cope alone at home and he tells me that they were sharing neighbouring beds when she died last week. It is said that on the scale of life crises moving home is second only to the bereavement of a loved one and

My family is the central thing in my life and general practice is almost an extension of that domesticity.

George has suffered both in the last seven days. Despite that, he appears remarkably stoical. He talks positively about his new home and is generous in his praise for the staff. He has a few of his personal possessions and photographs in his room and he shows me pictures of his daughter's family. They live locally and he expects to see them often.

The reason for my visit, as well as to meet each other, is that he is having trouble with his caliper and has been unable to walk any distance. The only remaining disabilty from his stroke is a weakness in the right leg. His ankle has no strength at all, but, wearing the caliper for support, and with the aid of a walking stick he has been fully mobile until now. I kneel down to undo the buckles and Velcro

fasteners and remove the boot and caliper. He has a nasty ulcer developing on the outer side of the ankle where it is rubbing. The boot is well worn and has become weakened and unsupporting. Also, he has developed a fluid swelling of the whole of the lower leg. His left leg is not so swollen and he is showing no sign of heart failure so I think this swelling is due to his loss of mobility. I prescribe a short course of diuretic medication to help reduce the fluid build-up and advise that he keeps the leg raised. I will arrange for the district nurses to attend to the ulcer and will get him an appointment with the surgical fitter in the next couple of weeks so that he can have a new boot and caliper fitted. I shall get on well with George.

My last visit is part medical and part social. Ronald and his wife Margaret are in their early eighties. They married only five years ago after Ronald's first wife died, and Margaret is totally dedicated to looking after him. For the last 10 years Ronald has had a benign form of leukaemia which has not caused him any great problem. He is a well-controlled diabetic patient – Margaret sees to that by meticulously regulating his diet – and he suffers from arthritis in his right hip joint. If that were not enough, two months ago he went into left-sided heart failure and had to be admitted to the coronary care unit at Musgrove Hospital with a build-up of fluid on his lungs. He has made an excellent recovery from the heart weakness and medication has cleared his lungs, but the whole process has knocked the stuffing out of him.

Margaret came secretly to see me in surgery earlier in the week to tell me that she can't get him motivated to move from his armchair. She wants him to walk out in the park and get fresh air, which she is sure will help.

'He says that his hip is too painful and says to me, "Anyway – why bother?" Also, he is not sleeping much and only picks at his food.'

I told Margaret that I would call round to see him in the next few days, and, after examining his heart, lungs and blood pressure I am able to reassure him that things are going well in that department. It is clearly a great relief to him and he visibly relaxes. We talk about the importance of getting mobile again and that he will not endanger his heart by doing gentle exercise. Minehead Hospital is a short walk from their flat and we agree that I will arrange some physiotherapy for his hip. This will give him good reason to get out of the flat and will help with the depressive reaction he is having to his recent illness. I don't think that he will need any antidepressive medication but I will review things in a fortnight's time.

Now to the social part of the call. Margaret makes the most wonderful home-made lemon curd and, once again, she has not let me down. She is waiting by the front door to see me out with a jar of the yellow confection in her hand and a smile on her face.

'Thank you so much for coming, doctor. I can already see that you have done him good.' The visit will also do me some good, as lemon meringue pie is my favorite pud!

The curd safely deposited in the car's glove compartment, I finally set off home. Hopefully I'll get a cuddle with Imogen and Jake will still be up and ready for a spot of puddle-stomping before his cruel mother and father insist on his going to bed. It is a glorious evening and the town centre is starting to fill up with people setting off on their Friday night jaunts. The main parade looks lovely during the summer and, as I drive up The Avenue, there are flowers everywhere you look. From the top of North Hill the sun is still reflecting off the sea and the view across the bay shows a sea that is mill-pond calm. By the time I've driven down my track that just about describes how I'm feeling. The stresses of the week forgotten, the weekend about to start and, best of all, Jakey at the window!

After sharing hugs and kisses with their parents, the serious business of active grandparenting begins. My daughter, who, it

The stresses of the week forgotten, the weekend about to start.

seems, so recently nestled on my chest with a handspan too small to encircle my little finger, who an eye's blink ago started school, is now Jake and Imogen's all-knowing mummy and not terribly impressed when grandad and Jakey become totally over-excited, leading to a case of violent hiccups and a vocal reluctance to start the bed-time ritual of bath and toothbrushing. Finally, however, bathed, changed and milked they are both tucked into their cots. With the children asleep, we now have our dinner and it is quite like old family meal times to have five of us sitting round the table.

With four children, you get used to having the house full up with them and their friends. There was a time when we never cooked for less than eight and extra chairs were always needed at meal times. As they grew up and started to leave home it was strange to set first five places, then four and now three. In many ways I think it must be harder for the youngest child – born into a bustling, noisy household of siblings, they suddenly find themselves alone with their parents. For old times' sake we play the alphabet game – going round the table naming in alphabetical order cars, countries or the cast of *EastEnders*. A new variation of the *EastEnders* game is for someone to name two characters and the winner is the first to work out how they are related – it can be done in most cases, although we are still looking for a link between Big Ron and the long-suffering Pauline (I strongly suspect that Martin will turn out to be their love-child). Finally we perform a family Mexican wave – high-powered stuff! Not the level of entertainment favoured by the chattering classes, but, I have to admit, good fun.

At work, as at home, it is not high-powered stuff. General practice is not glorious or high flying – it is not going to change the world. It is people based, often family based and is concerned with the day-to-day business of getting by and on with life. For me, my family is the central thing in my life; there is nowhere I would rather be than sitting at the kitchen table with them chattering away around me. General practice, and perhaps our practice in particular, is almost an extension of that sense of domesticity. We share the ups and downs of our patients, share problems large and small, and generally help people to keep ticking along. This year what we are doing has been put under the microscope, but usually the life of a general practitioner is not particularly newsworthy or notable. It is challenging and rewarding, but not particularly prestigious. It is stimulating and interesting, but not particularly exciting, but then I have never sought notoriety, prestige or excitement, so all in all it could be said to be 'just what the doctor ordered'.